The Essential Guide To Timber

Ed Scott

Glass House Books
Brisbane

Glass House Books
an imprint of IP (Interactive Publications Pty Ltd)
Treetop Studio • 9 Kuhler Court
Carindale, Queensland, Australia 4152
sales@ipoz.biz
ipoz.biz/GHB/GHB.htm

© 2022, Ed Scott (text and illustrations) and Interactive Publications (design)

ISBN 9781922332875 (HB); ISBN 9781922332882 (eBook)

A catalogue record for this book is available from the National Library of Australia

Contents

Acknowledgements

The author considers the book would not be complete without acknowledging the special assistance given by five highly qualified timber experts.

COLIN McKENZIE. With Colin's help the author was able to check the text in the great majority of the chapters for correctness and advise where changes were needed. Colin is a widely respected timber engineer with qualifications FIE Australia, CPEng, RPEG and NPER. He worked for many years in CSIRO Melbourne in the Forest Products Division.

KEVIN LYNGCOLN kindly checked the text in the plywood section and as a result changes were made and extra information included. Kevin is highly qualified with MIE[Aust] CP Eng. He was CEO of the Plywood Association of Australia for 33 years. He also assists UNESCO in setting up plywood industries in third world countries using local timbers.

JACK NORTON has a Degree in Applied Science and was Chief Chemist of the Forestry Department in Queensland for many years. He has been the President of International Research Group on Wood Protection and Secretary of The Timber Preservers Association of Australia. Jack kindly checked and helped with advice in the section of the text covering wood preservation.

MICHAEL KENNEDY has a Degree in Applied Science and was the Research Manager for 10 years in the Qld. Forestry Department until he recently retired. Michael kindly checked the text in Chapter 1 on Trees.

LEX SOMERVILLE provided the very professional drawings and illustrations throughout the book. Lex is fully licensed builder with extra qualifications including certificates visual stress grading of timber and Kiln Drying of timber. Lex worked for many years the Timber Research and Advisory Council who produced a large number of timber advisory brochures. Lex was heavily involved in their production.

With the exception of Michael Kennedy all the above experts have been closely associated with the author through his positions as managing the Queensland branch of various Australian timber companies.

Preface

Timber is a great natural raw material that has always been friendly to the world's environment. It has been utilized since mankind first walked on the planet. It has served as a source of fuel and to build shelters from the elements. Long before this, as prehistoric forests were progressively buried under rocks and sediments, they became the source of the large deposits of coal that now exist. The mining of these deposits is currently providing a major source of mankind's need for energy in many countries. Some of the species of trees from prehistoric times fifty million years ago such as the maidenhair tree [*Ginkgo Biloba*] and the Macrazamia bushes are still around today. They are often referred to as living fossils. Fossils of ginkgo leaves and leaves of other prehistoric plants can still be discovered in sedimentary rocks where the ground has been excavated. For example, fossils of the leaves of gingko biloba can be uncovered in one Brisbane quarry. The source of the photo of *Ginkgo Biloba* was the *Oxford Encyclopedia of trees of the world* and this is thankfully acknowledged. The photo of the Macrazamia came from the author's own garden.

Macrazamia

Ginko Biloba

Over the centuries going back before the time of the Pharaohs, timber has been widely used in building and for a wide range of other uses. One of the major attractions is its ease of workability so that all types of craftsmen can fashion it into a myriad of projects. It is also a good thermal and acoustic insulator. The great voyages of discovery in the fifteenth to seventeenth centuries were made in ships made out of timber. Men like Christopher Columbus and James Cook depended on the strength of timbers like English Oak and European Oak to venture on the world's great oceans. The great galleons and warships of a few centuries ago were also made of timber. However, it is of interest to note that over 200 years ago the demand for desired species such as English Oak became so great that the forests began to be badly depleted. As a result, the first steps at conservation came into being and the harvesting of species like English Oak had to be strictly controlled.

Apart from its strength and durability the decorative appearance of large numbers of different species has and still is favoured in all kinds of uses. The utilization of these decorative properties can be found in the interior fit outs of the world's great cathedrals where the strength of the timber is also utilized in much of the basic structures. The world heritage listed Sydney Opera House is a modern prime example of decorative and acoustic use of wood in that the interior largely features the use of brush box plywood. A more recent Australian structure is the Canberra Arboretum building where glue laminated timbers has been used in its roof structure. To conserve the resource of scarcer decorative species the slicing and peeling of veneers is now widespread worldwide. By using veneers glued to various types of substrates rather than solid timber the limited resource is greatly expanded.

Over the last century steel, concrete and masonry have made major inroads into uses which were traditionally covered by timber. In spite of this, the use of timber is ever increasing with a myriad of uses which range from a basic construction material to its use for conversion into other products such as board, plywood and paper. In some countries it is still very much the only fuel used for heating and cooking and meal preparation. In more recent times the development of cross laminated timber has resulted in the use of timber in medium rise multistory buildings, a market previously the preserve of steel and concrete. To cope with this demand, timber plantations have and continue to be established. While these are predominately softwood species, some are hardwood plantations. One of the major advantages of using timber is that it is a renewable resource. For it to remain so depends greatly on mankind's responsible and proper management of the world's existing forests and the continued development of forests of plantation timbers.

Introduction

With such a great natural resource available for so many different applications it is only sensible that the timber be used correctly and efficiently and that the resource not be wasted. To achieve this it is essential that users understand the product and that architects and timber designers also be knowledgeable on the many technical implications involved in the use of timber. They are then better equipped to ensure success in the multitude projects they work on. This list of projects in which timber can be used is immense. For example, it can range from major structures through to domestic housing and associated items such as floors, decks and other outdoor structures. Another large use of timber is in furniture manufacture and it is regularly used in craft activities like wood turning.

The purpose in writing this book, after encouragement from a well-known Central Queensland architect, was to commit to written form timber information the author had been fortunate to acquire through formal education and many years experience in different roles in the industry. Firstly, it would be interesting and helpful to users of timber and also those involved in the design phase. Secondly, it would, by providing essential information, help ensure timber and associated board products are used correctly and so help prevent problems occurring. Thirdly, as others gradually succeed the current small group of people highly qualified in timber technology, it would be an added source of technical information. The current small group provdes an essential service to the industry at large by providing information to designers and users, investigating site timber problems when they occur, preparing explanatory literature, assisting in the development of new standards, plus many more technical needs. In writing this book, it also became apparent that many critical sections where specific essential information was needed had to be covered. One example of this is the relationship of timber with moisture and the many aspects of this relationship. There are also several other critical sections that needed to be included. Thus, the original intent of the book, that it just be an interesting read for designers and users, was changed so that all this critical and essential information is covered. Hence the title *The Essential Guide to Timber*. It is hoped by careful study of relevant sections and frequent reference to the book that it will go a long way to achieving the efficient and correct use of timber.

By studying timber from the aspect of cell structure an explanation of many properties of timber becomes apparent. In particular the close relationship between timber and moisture becomes clear. Also, it gives an insight into why different species have different properties such as differences in decay resistance and resistance to termites and insects. An endeavour is made to not only provide the necessary factual information but also explain the reason why.

While much information about timber can be found by accessing the internet it is only as uncoordinated pieces of information. However, in studying the book all the information is grouped together so that it is easy in reading it to pass from one subject to associated subjects. While the book is essentially a 'textbook' every effort has been made to not write in typical textbook style. The book has been written in simple understandable free flowing language illustrated with plenty of photographs and a number of diagrams. The purpose in doing this was to make it easily understood and try and ensure that as wide a range of timber users as possible might be able to easily comprehend all the subjects covered. The great majority of all the photographs were taken by the author. For copyright reasons the source of other photographs and the diagrams have to have the approval of the company or person responsible. This has proved to be extremely difficult as many of the companies and people no longer exist. Where possible this approval has been secured.

Over recent years many changes have occurred in the timber industry. One of these has been a change in methods of marketing. Once timber was only available from timber merchants with staff specially trained in timber knowledge to disseminate information about timber. While timber merchants with staff trained in timber knowledge still operate, the current situation is that much of timber is now being mass merchandised with few people on hand with timber knowledge. The book therefore serves another useful purpose. If the buyer is unsure of what timber or species to purchase reference to the relevant section in the book can certainly help. The appendix is useful in this regard as it lists a wide range of different timbers with the different properties of each.

However, while the above comments are pertinent the author freely acknowledges that many architects, designers and builders have acquired a wide range of essential knowledge about timber over many years so they have little trouble in specification or purchasing the correct timber for the specific applications. However, it is still possible that some sections of the book can add further to their knowledge.

While access to essential knowledge is essential in the successful use of timber it is the author's opinion that this concept basically applies to all types of human endeavour. With this knowledge the necessary planning can be then carried out to enable projects to proceed. Whether it be putting a man on the moon or constructing major works like dams, bridges and skyscrapers. The key to all this is having easy accessibility to all of this relevant essential knowledge and then using it. Many of the major catastrophes that have occurred over the years have resulted from not having this essential knowledge or intentionally or unintentionally not using it. Failure of many bridges around the world, fires in the facades of high-rise buildings, collapse of multistory buildings in some countries, failure of tailing dam walls associated with mining operations are just a few examples in recent years. Many of these resulted in considerable loss of life. It is still happening. Needless to say the timber construction has not been immune to construction problems but generally without such dire consequences. For the interest of readers a few case studies of where timber problems have occurred have been included in Chapter 11.

Some 50 years ago the Department of Forestry in NSW realized that due to lack of information designers and users were not capitalizing on the availability of the great range of excellent NSW hardwoods available. One of their officers, Keith Bootle, who had a great depth of timber knowledge was commissioned to produce a book giving the necessary information. As well as information on NSW hardwoods, Keith also took the opportunity to include a lot of other information in the book including technical information about timber. This book served a real need and was widely read. The book was revised some 17 years ago. However, progress in the timber industry continues and there have been many important developments since then as for example cross laminated timber, changes in milling practices and new or revised Australian standards.

In producing the *Essential Guide* a somewhat different approach to that adopted in the NSW Forestry publication has been taken. As mentioned previously considerable importance is placed on the how much the cell structure of timber is integrated into so many of the properties of timber. Readers are encouraged to study the text so they not only have access to all of the various properties of timber but also understand the reason 'why.' The guide also includes chapters on the range of board products especially plywood and veneers, glue laminated products and also a chapter devoted to working with timber. In short, the Essential Guide is quite different in many ways from the excellent NSW Forestry publication that was produced many years ago. It is also intended that it be equally suitable for use in any Australian state.

The author was encouraged to put this book together by a well-known central Queensland architect Mr. Brian Hooper. Mr. Hooper won awards for the design of a well-known timber structure in Barcaldine in central Queensland called the Tree of Knowledge. Because there are some 3600 pieces 125mm x 125mm pieces of hardwood hanging from supports above and the public are free to walk underneath there was a real need to check for any dangerous splits and checks particularly around the support points that could cause these very heavy pieces of timber to drop. On one of the early visits to the site with Mr. Hooper the author to his surprise found himself explaining all kinds of basic terms and technical details about timber that he thought most architects knew. He was assured this was not the case and he felt that many of his associates were in the same position. He suggested that, as he felt the author had acquired considerable knowledge on this subject, he commit it to writing in the form of a book.

This discussion then also helped the author better understand after carrying out hundreds of on-site inspections over many years throughout Queensland and in northern New South Wales why timber problems had arisen. These requests emanated from a wide range of sources particularly Government Building authorities who are the usual arbiters when disputes arise. The reason why problems occurred was that, in spite of the best of intents, the architect, designer or builder did not have enough of an understanding of the properties of timber or the recommended procedures for the project in hand. In providing all this essential information in an easily readable book for all to use, it is hoped it will provide a quick handy source of this essential information.

In setting about the project, it was realized that with the great diversity of subjects and the sheer amount of information involved, no one person would be adequately qualified and that a lot of help would be needed. This has been freely supplied and has come from a wide range of sources including Australia's major millers, foresters, specialists in the timber industry, timber industry associations and major machinery manufacturers.

When considering the many uses of timber, it is also considered important that the community at large look favourably on using timber as a construction material rather than steel or concrete particularly as timber is a renewable resource. In addition, by so doing they also ensure the health of the timber industry which is a major contributor to Australia's economy. This favourable perception by the community depends very much on the correct use of timber in its many applications. This in turn depends on the designer, the builder, the user and the timber supplier having a thorough understanding of timber and its many properties. Hopefully in some small way the Essential Guide can make a contribution.

Lastly great care and attention has been taken that as far as possible what has been written is correct and to this end the author is indebted to a number of highly qualified people in the timber industry for checking various sections of the subjects covered.

Preview of Chapters

The determination of what subjects should be included was difficult. The amount of information that it would be possible to include is immense and beyond being included in one book of a reasonable size. A list of subjects which it was felt would cover the book's objectives viz to give readers a thorough knowledge of timber was selected. Included in the list also were subjects such as plywood, board products and glue laminated products because of the essential role they now frequently play in the timber construction process.

It was felt that a quick review of what is covered in each of the chapters would be helpful so that before becoming very familiar with the guide the reader can quickly find the best chapter or chapters for reference.

Chapter 1: Trees

Although this is not essential reading it was considered that as it is the source of the product by having some knowledge of how trees fit into the plant kingdom would be helpful. The chapter also covers the essential difference between hardwoods and softwoods which many using timber do not accurately understand.

A simplified explanation of photosynthesis, the role of CO_2 in the growth of a tree and how a tree grows is included.

Chapter 2: Timber Mill Operations

Having a knowledge of what goes on in the timber mill is very useful in understanding what the buyer's expectations should be as regards quality and delivery. The chapter also covers a little bit of interesting history over what used to be and the advances that have taken place over the years. The current situation is now that most timber mills are now a very highly sophisticated operations with computer-controlled milling and handling and in the case of plantation pines automatic optical scanning for grading of both the product being produced and the logs before milling. This is included in some detail.

Chapter 3: Seasoning and Grading of Timber

This chapter is divided into two sections. The first covers seasoned and unseasoned timber and details the advantages and disadvantages of each and where they are used. There is also a section on the different methods of seasoning. The second section lists the four main standards used in grading hardwoods and softwoods including a brief outline of what is included in each standard and methods of grading. The chapter finishes with a complete list of current standards as advised by the Standards Association and includes what each applies to. Also listed is where copies of the standards can be obtained.

Chapter 4: The Structure of Timber

This is an important chapter as it explains the cell structure of a piece of timber, the different types of cells and the different organic chemicals involved in the cell structure plus other chemicals found in the cells and of what importance these are. It also explains which parts of tree where the cells are formed. The difference between cells in the truewood [heartwood] and the sapwood and why there is a difference is explained. Also covered is the important difference in cells found in softwoods and hardwoods. Having a knowledge of the cell structure of timber gives a better understanding of the different properties of timber.

Chapter 5: The Properties of Timber

Like Chapter 4 this chapter explains a great amount of information that every designer or user should thoroughly understand. It covers the more important properties such as density, strength, hardness, toughness and appearance. Chapters 6, 7 and 8 cover other important properties such as decay resistance and timber's relation to moisture. Strength subjects like modulus of rupture [MOR] and modulus of elasticity [MOE] are covered as well as other strength factors. The classification of strength groups and how they relate to stress groups plus the terminology of MGP are explained. There is also a section on how timber dimensions affect load carrying capacity. Finally, hardness, toughness and appearance [colour, grain, texture and figure] are covered. There is much to study and understand in this chapter.

Chapter 6: Timber and Moisture

This chapter covers the close relationship between timber and moisture content and how it is entirely different to metals. Some of the factors covered include definition of moisture content and methods of measuring it. The various moisture meters in common use and principals of operation are listed. The next section leads to the percentage of moisture in timber as sawn and examples of typical moisture contents of various species. The concept of fibre saturation point and how this is associated with the cell structure is explained. Next is the relative difference in shrinkage as timber seasons between length, breadth and length. The concept of equilibrium moisture content [EMC], what it means, how it is calculated and its importance in using seasoned timber is explained. The movement of seasoned timber with changes in atmospheric conditions is also covered as is the term unit shrinkage. Lastly typical shrinkage of a range of common timbers from unseasoned [green] to seasoned are listed. Understanding all the points in this chapter is very important in the successful use of timber.

Chapter 7: Degradation of Timber

The degradation of timber in service is split into two sections. Firstly, is the decay by fungi and a section on timber preservation. Fungal attack covers how it happens and conditions necessary for it to occur. The different types of fungi are listed and described. The concept of classes of decay resistance with listings for the different timbers is set out. This includes the in ground and out of ground resistance of more common species. Also in this first section is a very comprehensive section on preservative treatment including the chemicals used, methods of treatment and the H [hazard] listing H1 to H6.

In the second section other factors which lead to attack of timber are covered including insects, termites, marine organisms, weathering by exposure to the elements and finally a short section on fire. Each section is covered in detail as for example in the case of termites the different types, termite resistant timbers, the Australian Standard and methods of prevention. This is a very informative chapter and covers many situations where mistakes are made in the construction process.

Chapter 8: Working with Timber

This chapter has two objectives, firstly to assist those with a limited knowledge about the regular tools used in woodwork viz. saws, planers, moulders and routers. It sets out the different terms used and what they mean. Secondly, in the section on turning it covers the factors that have to be covered when turning. There is also a list of regular timbers used in turning along with their properties. Lastly, there is a short section on health and safety as it applies to sawdust and sander dust. This also includes a list rating a number of regularly used species.

Chapter 9: Fabricated Timber Products

This is a comprehensive coverage of the range of board products available viz. plywood, particleboard, fibreboard, hardboard and bamboo composite board. The section covers the method of manufacture, grades, properties, the range of products commonly available plus the reaction of each with moisture. There is also a special section on decorative veneers, how they are produced, their application and illustrations of popular veneers.

Chapter 10: Glue Laminated Timber Products

In this chapter is the range of typical products made by glue laminating solid timber or veneers into typical timber sizes. It covers the traditional laminated beams plus newer products such as laminated veneer lumber [LVL] and Cross Laminated Timber [CLT]. Methods of manufacture, properties and uses are covered. Also included in this chapter is the very important subject of Finger Jointing.

Chapter 11: Case Studies – Examination of Situations Where Problems Occurred

This chapter gives readers the opportunity to review actual case histories where serious problems occurred and refer to the pertinent chapters in the guide relating to the problems involved. By studying the cases and working out why the mistakes occurred hopefully it will help readers in ensuring they do not become involved in similar situations.

Appendices 1 and 2

The two appendices list some 22 commonly available Australian hardwoods, six Australian softwoods and eight imported timbers. In addition to the botanical name, some 12 properties of are listed such strength group, density, shrinkage green to dry, durability etc. This provides a quick and easy ready reference for use by readers.

Subjects Not Covered

Firstly, although some elementary principles on timber strength and deflection were covered in Chapter 4, no in-depth attempt has been made to include timber engineering detail as this is a major discipline in its own right which really requires basic engineering qualifications. Secondly, details of recommended procedures for all types of timber construction could not be included. These procedures cover such items as the light timber framing code covering house construction, the laying of timber floors, construction of decks, pergolas and carports, exterior cladding, fencing, timber landscaping walls and many more. The number of different procedures available and the scope of the procedures qualify them as a major publication in their own right. Some of these procedures can be referenced from the *National Construction Code - Building Code of Australia*, others from some of the relevant Australian Standards such as AS1684, the *Timber Framing Code*, from the Wood Solutions organization or from the State Timber Marketing Associations. With a knowledge of information contained in the Essential Guide it does give an insight into why many of the requirements set out in the procedures are necessary. The guide is also useful in explaining terms in the guides that may not be clearly understood.

Progress in Timber Technology

The science and engineering of timber has come a long way over the last few decades and a great deal of research is still being carried out. For example, the development of glued cross laminated timber [CLT] and techniques to use it in multistory buildings represented a major advance. This is covered in Chapter 10. The development of water based acrylic finishes has also been a great step forward particularly with outside finishes. It has greatly extended the life of the paint film and in so doing has not only ensured a longer lasting satisfactory appearance but also reduced the cost of exterior maintenance of timber.

Preservation of timber has also seen great advances and improvements in safety of the products used for preservation.

Guide Preparation and Disclaimer

In the preparation of this *Essential Guide* a great amount of care has been taken in include all the information that was considered essential and to further try and ensure the text is as accurate as possible. The help of recognized authorities in the different subjects has been sought to check over what has been written. The list of those who assisted has been acknowledged in the Bibliography and without their help the book could not have been completed. However, with all the variables that can occur in the use of timber, often unknown, no legal liability can be accepted if problems arise with the use and/or interpretation of the great amount of information documented in this Essential Guide.

Getting the Most Benefit in Using *The Guide*

Obviously, every reader will have their own ideas on how to gain most use and benefit from the *Essential Guide* particularly as different readers will be viewing from a different perspective. Hopefully perusing the preview of each of the chapters above will help the user to quickly access the information required. However, in using the *Guide* it will frequently be found necessary to use information from more than one chapter. It is also hoped that it will serve as an educational tool. Over a period of time, by progressive use of the various chapters of the *Essential Guide*, it is sincerely hoped that the innocent dissemination of incorrect information about timber properties can be corrected and that all readers will gain a better understanding of timber as this is the reason the book was written.

CHAPTER 1: TREES

Whether it be a beautiful grand piano, a residential deck, a medium rise building constructed using timber or even landscaping sleepers the timber was there to use because many years ago a tree was planted or a seed or cone dropped. In brief as everyone knows trees are where timber comes from.

The purpose of this chapter is to give a little understanding of trees and how they fit into the plant kingdom. However, it is not proposed to delve deeply into the botanical aspects of trees and their growth as this is a vast subject in its own right as well as being incredibly complex.

In brief and simple terms an attempt will be made to just cover the following subjects

- The classification of plants and where trees fit in
- The basics of tree growth
- The various parts of the tree.

The Classification of Trees and Plants

In the botanical kingdom there are two main classes of plants viz. gymnosperms and angiosperms. The division is based on whether the seeds are not covered [naked seeds] as in the gymnosperms or covered [vessel seeds] as in the angiosperms. Fertilisation to produce the seed in the angiograms is carried out in flowers rather than in cones so the angiograms are also known as the flowering plants. Pollination in the gymnosperms from the male cone to the female cone is brought about by wind whereas in the angiosperms flowers it is carried out by insects particularly bees. The importance of bees is illustrated in California where once a year the apiarists from across the U.S.A. bring their bees across to ensure fertilization of the almond groves. This also happens in many other countries as in Australia where beehives are trucked in to Victoria, primarily from Queensland, to fertilise the large groves of almond trees.

In the plant kingdom there are less than 1000 gymnosperms known but hundreds of thousands of angiosperms. As far as trees are concerned common examples of gymnosperms are conifers such as the pines, firs, spruces, cedars and redwoods where the seeds are developed in the cones. Typical examples of angiosperms are the Australian eucalypts, the American and English oaks and the wide variety of trees in the tropical rainforests of the world providing timbers such as meranti, mahogany, merbau etc., The highly prized ornamental street tree, the Poinciana, is a great example of seeing how the seeds are enclosed in seed pods. In fruit bearing trees such as citrus and the stone fruits the seed is covered in the fruit.

The angiosperms are further divided into two major groups viz. Monocotyledons [one shoot plants] where the seed sends produces only one leaf as it germinates and Dicotyledons where two leaves arise from the seed. Monocotyledons include such tree like plants as palms and grass trees and more obviously grassy plants such as the bamboos, the grasses and grain crops such as wheat and corn. Dicotyledons include all the hardwood tree species of which the Australian eucalypts are a notable example. In botanical terms the gymnosperms such as the pines, spruces, firs, cedars and redwood are classified as softwoods. Trees in the angiosperm class are designated as hardwoods. This classification bears no relation to the relative hardness or softness of the timbers produced. For example, some botanically classed hardwoods are quite 'soft' e.g., balsa and some pines classified as softwoods are relatively 'hard.' To determine hardness of a species, reference has to be made to timber hardness tables that have been produced and these have nothing to do with botanical classification.

Trees can then be illustrated as follows

Gymnosperms	Angiosperms
The Softwoods [Conifers And Yews]	The Hardwoods Dicotyledons
Pines Spruces & Firs	Hardwood Trees
Cedars & Redwoods	Eucalypts
Cycads	Oaks Ashes, Etc.

As noted above in the plant kingdom the grain crops such as wheat, barley and rye etc., and the various grasses fall into the monocotyledon classification

The Basics of Tree Growth

The processes that take place in the growth of a tree are incredibly complicated and really only understood by very qualified botanists and experts in the field. However, it is helpful if those involved in the use of timber have a general idea of how a tree grows. A very highly simplified version follows. Obviously as the tree grows the height increases, branches are developed the diameter increases and the root system has to increase in size to anchor the tree and provide the extra nutrients from the soil.

Three Sections of a Tree

The main three sections of a tree are as follows.
- The crown, branches and the associated foliage

- The trunk
- The root system

The crown, the ends of the branches and the associated foliage is where the solar energy of the sun is converted to chemical energy by photosynthesis in the leaves or needles. Carbon dioxide in the atmosphere plus moisture from the air and brought up from the ground from the roots are changed into complex food materials such as sugars and starch. These materials are required for development into cells required for the growth of the tree. In this area the topmost shoots extend the length of the trunk and more branches may develop. It is also the area where flowers develop and fertilisation and seed production happens. It is this area that the genetics of the individual species are stored. The presence of chlorophyll in the leaves is considered essential for photosynthesis. When it is considered that a single leaf can have well over a million cells and in deciduous trees all the leaves are replaced annually some concept of the incredible and complicated processes that are involved in tree growth can be imagined.

The trunk provides the structural support for the tree and also it is where moisture and nutrients are conducted up and down from the roots and the crown. The length of the trunk increases through continuous cell production in the crown and not by increase in the length and size of cells already in the trunk. The diameter increases by laying down of new cells on the outer perimeter of the trunk.

This means that if a piece of metal is hammered in to the trunk at a specific height, is progressively covered by increase in trunk diameter and many years later the tree is being milled the piece of metal will be found in exactly the same position above the ground where it was originally fixed. Of course, when milling this is not good for the saw and a understandable reluctance of sawmillers to take logs from areas where houses have been constructed.

Lastly, the roots serve to anchor the tree to the ground and provide essential nutrients and moisture from the soil. The necessary extension of the root system as the tree grows in size occurs by new cell production with photosynthesis products drawn down from the crown and moisture and nutrients taken up from the soil. The fine root hairs that develop on the roots are an important part of the root system and the processes that occur.

It is also a critical area where moisture, nutrients and other essential elements involved in the cell process such nitrogen, phosphorous, potassium etc., are taken from the soil and conducted upwards. Various types of fungi and microorganisms in the soil surrounding the roots assist in the take up of these essential chemicals from the soil.

Source of Timber

From the point of the timber user, the trunk is the source of the timber to be milled. However not all zones through the trunk are used in milling timber only the sapwood and truewood. However, for some uses, for example in wharf piles, the whole log including the outer bark layer is used.

A cross section through the trunk shows all these zones. This also provides an understanding of the processes that take place in the living tree and how the tree grows and increases in size from a tiny sapling to a forest giant. The sections are [from the outside in]:

- The outer bark
- The inner bark
- The cambium layer
- The sapwood
- The truewood [sometimes referred to as heartwood]
- The inner heart or pith

In strictly botanical terms the terms xylem and phloem refer to the specialized cells within the sapwood zone that function to move water, sugars and nutrients up and down.

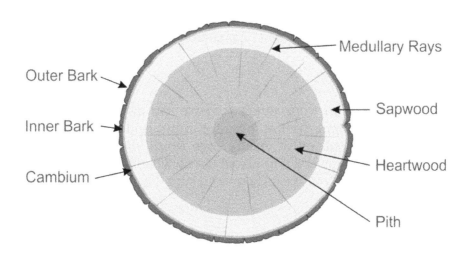

Tree Cross-section

The Outer Bark

This serves to protect the tree and its underlying critical layers from physical damage. As the tree expands in width this bark becomes too small for the underlying wood and has to be gradually replaced.

The Inner Bark

This is one zone where nutrients and moisture derived from the soil are moved upwards to the trunk and crown to be used in the production of new cells for tree growth .

The Cambium Layer

This layer of cells is responsible for the increase in diameter of the trunk. In this layer more cells are produced which initially have flexible walls allowing them to gradually expand in size until they reach maturity. When this occurs the secondary cell walls are laid down and stiffened with substances such as cellulose. They then take no further part in physically increasing the diameter. Another layer of flexible cells grows outside of these and so the process goes on.

It is interesting to observe that in spring and early summer when cell development is favourable the size of the cells can be larger than in autumn and winter giving rise to the terms early wood and late wood and the concept of annular rings. This also can be used to assess the age of the tree. If this layer of cells in the cambium is destroyed e.g., by ring barking, the tree will die.

The Sapwood

This is the part of the trunk where nutrients and moisture can continue to move up and down the tree from the crown and ends of branches. However, it is composed of mature cells which in themselves do not increase the diameter of the trunk but are continually being added to by succeeding layers of mature cells coming from the cambium layer.

The Truewood

As the tree increases in size the cells in the inner part of the sapwood progressively become filled with gums, resins and other substances and can longer serve to move nutrients for cell production up and down the tree. It is then called the truewood [or sometimes the heartwood] These materials in the cells often confer the ability to resist decay and attack by insects etc., both by being toxic to wood destroying organisms and by reducing the permeability of the wood to moisture movement.

The Inner Heart or Pith

This is a collection of cells which were originally present in the first stages of the growth of the tree. In mature trees e.g., eucalypts this inner heart contains an interior set of 'heartwood compounds' making this zone more vulnerable to decay and invasion by termites.

The processes that take place in using the carbon dioxide, oxygen, the moisture in the air and from chemicals and moisture in the soil plus the energy from the sun to produce the cell structure of the tree are extremely complex. The processes of fertilisation of the seed, the involvement of the gene process are also incredibly complex as are the mechanisms by which nutrients move up and down the tree through the cell structures. Because this book is primarily about the properties of timber and its use, a complete understanding of photosynthesis and the botanical processes that occur has not been attempted, only a few simple explanations. However, as a definition photosynthesis can be defined as the process where light energy from the sun is changed into chemical energy to produce a range of chemical products which are then used in the development of plant cell structure. For those wanting to venture deeper into plant physiology many excellent books exist [e.g., *Plant Physiology* by Taiz and Zeiger.]

The sapwood and the truewood in the trunk of the tree are the primary source of the timber used in commerce. The relative proportion of sapwood to truewood in the tree varies greatly according to the species and the age of the tree. Young rapidly growing trees have a greater percentage of sapwood when compared with old matured trees. As an example of the latter the log from an old matured grey ironbark tree up to one metre in diameter will generally only have an external sapwood band of about 20mm to 25mm wide. Many conifers e.g., pines tend to contain much more sapwood.

Mountain Ash

Heights and Ages of Australian Trees

It is interesting to look at the heights and ages of the trees in Australia and some interesting facts are found. Some Australian trees such as the Ashes in Victoria can range up to 100 metres or more. The Mountain Ash [*eucalyptus regnans*] is the tallest hardwood tree in the world. Generally, when fully grown most eucalypts are around 80 metres. However, none are as tall as the giant redwoods in California, which are up to 120 metres tall and the trunk at the ground level can have a circumference of 10 metres. The redwoods are classified as softwoods.

Australia has many very old trees. The curtain fig trees can be up to 1000 years old and the Mountain Ashes 400 years old. The oldest known trees are some specimens of Huon Pine in Tasmania which are considered to be close to 4000 years old. Where trees are being grown for production into timber, as for example the plantations of pine forests, these are normally harvested in well under 50 years. The source of the photo is the very excellent book *A Field Guide to Eucalypts* by Brooker and Kleinig (1999).

Factors Influencing Tree Growth Rates

The main factors influencing the rate of growth of trees are:

- hours of sunshine [for photosynthesis]
- rainfall
- soil fertility
- temperature.

The tropical rainforests provide a good example of favourable growing conditions and growth of species suited to this environment is rapid. It is of interest to note that many rainforest soils are relatively shallow so that buttressing is common to give the tree more anchorage. Buttressing is where roots extend upwards and are joined to the trunk. In some other species like figs tendrils extend down from the trunk and into the ground to give further support to the trunk giving the 'curtain fig effect'.

The conifer forests of North America provide a good example of how the influencing factors affect the size and rate of growth of trees. The giant Redwoods of California have favourable growing conditions – adequate sunlight, temperature, rainfall and good soil conditions. However, in areas closer to the Arctic Circle such as northern Canada and across into Siberia the rate of growth is very slow and overall tree heights are greatly reduced. This is due to lower annual hours of sunlight, greatly reduced temperatures and ground frozen for lengthy periods. Tree species that can survive under these conditions need to be conservative, safe and steady growers.

Chapter 2: Timber Mill Operations

Once the tree has been felled and transported to the sawmill or other manufacturing facility, the task of converting the trunk into commercial products can be undertaken. This involves four main procedures:

- sawing the log to produce sawn timber for commerce
- grading the timber
- drying the timber if a seasoned product is required
- dressing the timber to give a range of products [again, if required]
- preservative treatment if required.

Note that when the timber is graded is variable and the final grading may in some cases be carried out after the timber has been seasoned.

Alternatively, instead of the above processes, the log may be chipped for converting into paper or board products or peeled and or sliced for the manufacture of veneers, plywood or laminated veneer lumber [LVL]. There are quite a number of options

Before the log can be sawn it has, of course, be removed from the forest. This can in areas of rough terrain be difficult and may involve the use of overhead wires or the use of rivers and streams. As well as being available for local milling, in some areas with very large availability there can be a major business in the export of logs. This export of logs from one country to another is widespread internationally. However, to ensure long term sustainability of forest resources there are now controls on the logging of forests. Procedures have been put in place in most countries. Unfortunately, in some areas of the world some operators are still not following these procedures and forests are suffering. In addition, in some areas the sustainability of the forests is being severely impacted by clearing so that the area can be used for farming and grazing. However, in some areas of the world this is also a contentious subject as the existence and livelihood of the local indigenous inhabitants depends on being able to farm.

The Early Days of Sawmilling

Historically, there have been very significant improvements in sawmilling. Early methods involved slabbing with an axe or pit sawing. The latter involved suspending the log over a pit with one man under the log in the pit and one standing on the log. A large saw was then pulled up and down and the log cut along its length into planks. This was eventually replaced with a saw bench with a circular saw and the log was pushed through the saw. For many years steam engines were used to drive the saw. Eventually the conversion from steam driven power to electricity greatly improved the process. Over the years the use of the twin Canadian with two large circular saws one above the other has become popular for breaking down larger diameter hardwood logs.

Sawing the Log

Softwoods

The extensive plantations of various species of pine that have been developed in Australia means that a large proportion of timber used in construction comes from these sources. Originally only unseasoned hardwood was considered suitable by builders for house construction ['packing case timber 'as they called it was taboo.] However eventually the benefits of using lighter kiln dried pine were recognized. The availability of different strength grades was also attractive. The main species now used are radiata, caribbean and slash pine hybrids.

There are a number of other softwood species such as cypress pine, hoop pine, celery top pine etc., which are milled but usually in small mills. With the exception of cypress these are used in applications other than house framing.

For many years after transport to the mill, logs had the edges sawn off to make a square section and were then sawn using band or circular saws into the sizes required. After drying in a kiln, the timber was dressed, then graded into the various strength grades, stamped, docked to length and then the different grades separated and bundled for dispatch into the construction industry. A proportion of the higher-grade timber was separated out and then dried and machined for use in mouldings, flooring, cladding and other uses. Some of the log supply for uses where unseasoned timber is required such as fencing and landscaping was segregated, preservative treated and then sawn into the sizes required. This use does not require drying or machining. This overall procedure was common for many years.

In more recent times with new mills being built and older ones upgraded, while the log has still to be sawn, dried, dressed and graded, very significant technical advances are being incorporated. These include the following:

Separation of the timber from high quality logs from timber from low quality logs before processing. This is done when the initial sawing to square up the log and remove the edges occurs and is done by optically scanning. Timber suitable for producing framing timber is segregated from timber that will be used for landscaping. Log quality varies in that some trees produce high strength timber, others produce lower quality. While this has been known ever since the exotic pines were first processed the differences in quality usually only showed up when the timber had been through all the processes viz. sawing, drying, dressing and the final grading. There was no sure method of separating out the lower quality logs before processing. This problem has now been overcome. Higher quality timber that has been segregated is now sawn into the different sizes required and kiln dried. The last step is dressing the timber and at this stage the timber is graded into the different strength groups MGP 10, 12 and 15. Timber for lower grade use such as landscaping is sawn into the range of sizes required which may not even require drying. Normally as pine is classified to be of low durability in external situations, this timber has to be preservative treated.

While not yet in wide use in Australia very highly sophisticated equipment has been developed where the saw follows the direction of the grain in each log resulting in a higher production of high stress grade timber. If the grain direction is exactly parallel to the length of the sawn piece the greatest strength is produced.

Another relatively new innovation is the grading of timber by computer controlled optical analysis as was mentioned above in the processing of pine. This progressively views the timber as it moves along, checks the various factors that affect grade such as knots, slope of grain and other natural defects and refers them to the grading rules in the computer so that each piece is graded once it issues from the machine. This is faster, more reliable and economical than manual grading. Not all mills are so equipped and these still rely on manual or the computermatic stress grading to determine the various stress grades.

Some mills are now 'squaring up the log' for the saws using special chipping machines so that the edges of the logs are immediately available for further manufacture where chips are the feed stock.

Sawing Hardwoods

Because of the weight of most hardwood logs special equipment is commonly required to get the log to the saw bench. There are a range of saws used from the regular circular saws, the twin Canadian saws [one mounted immediately above the lower saw,] the band saw or even gang saws. The saws chosen depend on many factors including the scale of the milling operations, the typical size and the species of log being processed and whether the mill is relatively new or has been operating for a long time.

Methods of Sawing

There are two methods of sawing that are used. Firstly back [tangential] sawing and secondly quarter sawing. Back sawing means sawing the timber tangential to the circumference of the log. Quarter sawing means sawing in the radial direction i.e.in to the centre of the log. This means that with back sawn timber that the width of the piece is tangential to the growth rings and the thickness then becomes quarter sawn. With quarter sawn the opposite occurs with the width cut in the direction from the surface of the log to the centre. This is much easier to understand by referring to the illustration shown below. The diagram shows the width of the piece not the thickness.

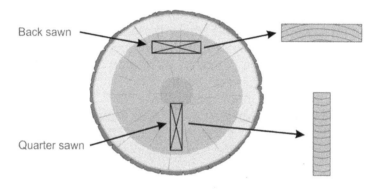

Back and Quarter Sawing

The significant difference is that with back sawn timber as the shrinkage in the tangential direction is twice that in the radial direction the percentage shrinkage in the width is twice as much as that which occurs in the depth. If the shrinkage of the speciesis in the low to moderate range [i.e., under 10% from green to dry] then the shrinkage that occurs during seasoning can be accommodated. However this is not the case with high shrinkage species like mountain and alpine ash species in Victoria and Tasmanian oak species in Tasmania where the shrinkage is commonly around 13%. These are usually quarter sawn to reduce the reduction in width that would occur if they were back sawn. This means when these species are cut as for boards for flooring, decking and joinery the loss in width in seasoning is much less. This then saves the extra costs involved in sawing wider boards to ensure that after drying and machining in the standard widths that are required can be minimised. With the typical thickness which is usually only a quarter of the width or less, shrinkage is not so critical. With heavier sections such as beams or joists where the depth of the member for strength purposes is very important the same reasoning applies even though the timber is usually supplied without seasoning. There is less shrinkage in depth for high shrinkage timbers as they season after use if they are quarter sawn. However with lower shrinkage hardwoods the normal back sawing is carried out.

New Advances in Sawing

While there has not been the same level of advanced techniques that have happened in the milling of softwoods many new innovations have nevertheless occurred. As regards sawing many of the smaller sawmills are still using the conventional saw bench and circular saws. Docking to length after sawing is still controlled manually. However, there has been a lot of improvements made in sawing techniques used in larger mills. These include:

- Widespread use of computers to automatically control operations from the initial squaring up in conjunction with laser beams, the actual sawing and the docking and sorting after the initial sawing. This applies to mills using either band saws or twin Canadian circular saws.
- The development of the radial sawmill that cuts the log into wedges which results in less wastage particularly with larger logs in 'squaring' the log. This is also helpful where quarter sawing of higher shrinkage timbers is necessary.

Grading

In the case of softwoods there have been great advances in the methods of grading with some particularly the newer mills using computer controlled optical graders as detailed in the section on sawing softwoods. Overall, the use of computers and the latest machinery has greatly automated the operations that take place after the timber has been sawn, dried, dressed or graded. The product at the different stages is automatically directed to different areas for the next stage in the overall processing.

As pointed out earlier grading can take place either before or after the drying process occurs and in the processing of pine takes place both before and after seasoning.

Kiln Drying

Many mills are now using computers to automatically control the kiln drying operations using specific programmes for the various species. These control the temperatures and air flows at the various stages of the process according to the species of timber being dried. With softwoods there is the use of weights on the top of packs to minimize twisting and keep the timber straight.

A large proportion of the hardwood that is milled is now sold as a seasoned dressed product to better utilize the resources available and realize a higher return. This includes products such as flooring, decking, internal joinery, furniture grades and some seasoned framing timber. There are still some mills using air drying instead of or in conjunction with kilns.

Dressing and Machining

There have been improvements in the cutters to give better finishes for the various Australian hardwoods which vary in hardness and difficulty in machining from medium density hardwoods such as Tasmanian oak through to the very hard high density species such as the Ironbarks. Rates of feed in are also automatically controlled to meet predetermined recommended speeds.

Preservative Treatment of Hardwoods and Softwoods

Hardwoods

Preservative treatment is also carried out in many mills where the sapwood of some hardwood species requires treatment to prevent attack by some insects. If the sapwood is being included in applications destined for exterior application then it requires preservative treatment. This is because the sapwood of hardwoods is not durable in external applications such as decking.

Softwoods

In the case of softwoods, as they are not durable against fungal attack if they are to be used in exterior conditions or in situations where protection against infestation by some insects is required then preservative treatment is necessary. Full information on preservative treatment is covered in Chapter 7.

Chapter 3: Unseasoned and Seasoned Timber and Timber Grading

This chapter is divided into two sections and covers the following subjects:

Section A

- The seasoning of timber
- Methods of seasoning timber
- The choice between unseasoned and seasoned timbers.

Section B

- The grading of timber according to the relevant standards
- A listing of most of the standards in use
- Details of some the more common standards in general use.

NOTE: Chapter 6 covering Timber and Moisture also gives more information on some of the matters covered in this chapter.

The Seasoning of Timber

Dependent on the species involved freshly sawn timber as it comes from the tree can have a moisture content which can range from 30% to over 150%. In other words, with some species, there is more water present than the wood substance itself. Timber shrinks as it loses moisture and the dimensions change. Therefore real benefits can be achieved in removing most of this moisture by seasoning and eliminating this shrinkage.

Defining Moisture Content

Several ways have evolved over time in defining moisture content. One was the weight of the water as a percentage of the total weight of the wood plus the water. The weight of the water was secured by oven drying a sample. So if the sample of wood plus the water was 100 grams and weight of the water was 30 grams the percentage water was 30%. This method always gave a percentage less than 100%. However the acknowledged method now is to use the following formula.

$$\% \text{ moisture content} = \frac{\text{initial weight} - \text{the oven dry weight} \times 100}{\text{oven dry weight}}$$

As an example consider a case where the initial weight was 100 grams and the oven dry weight was 80 grams. Using the formula above:

$$\% \text{ moisture content} = \frac{100 - 80}{80} \times 100 = \frac{20 \times 100}{80} = 25\%$$

Slight variations of this formula do exist but they end up giving the same result. However it must be kept in mind that in practice on site moisture contents are usually determined by a moisture meter. Thus the foregoing only applies when it is desired to use the results of an oven dry test and apply the formula quoted above for some particular reason.

Defining the Term Seasoned

Most standards refer to seasoned timber as timber whose moisture content has been reduced to between 10% and 15%. Seasoned timber is also commonly referred to as kiln dried [KD] even though it may not have been dried in a kiln.

At the timber mill whether or not the timber will then be seasoned depends very much on the species being processed and the intended market for the timber. For example, as discussed in chapter 2 in processing of the plantation pines the higher quality logs are cut into timber framing sizes and seasoned, the lower grades may be cut into sizes suitable for fencing and landscaping, left unseasoned and then preservative treated. In the case of hardwoods some mills may cut the timber into sizes suitable for unseasoned hardwood market others may, if the species are suitable, choose to process the timber for the higher-grade markets such as flooring, furniture, paneling, decking and joinery. This then involves cutting into the required sizes and seasoning it. In effect whether or not the timber being cut at the mill is to be further processed by seasoning or left unseasoned depends on many factors.

Factors involved in the seasoning process include:

- Density – the denser the timber the longer it takes to season
- Cross section size – larger sections take longer. Seasoning hardwood in sizes over 50mm in thickness is usually not commercially viable due to the length of time taken and the degrade of a percentage of the timber that occurs during the seasoning process.
- The timber specie
- The weather conditions where seasoning is to take place. If air drying is being undertaken hot dry conditions obviously require different procedures drying to cold wetter conditions.

All the above factors have to be considered.

Methods of Seasoning Timber

There are basically two processes used viz. air drying and kiln drying. The first involves putting out timber in stacks which then dries as the air circulates through the stack, the second putting the stack in a kiln, generating hot air and then using fans to push the hot air through the stack.

Air Drying

Using the air-drying procedure is more economical in terms of facilities required and there is no cost for heating and moving the air but the process is very much slower. However, offsetting this is the capital cost of the timber held in stock plus uncertainty in delivery schedules due to changes in weather conditions.

The Air-Drying Process

Briefly the usual process involves

- Use of a sufficiently sized area of level well drained land well exposed to the prevailing winds
- Building a structurally adequate foundation on which to place the stack
- Building the stack for the timber requiring seasoning
- Providing a waterproof cover over the stack to keep out the rain and protect the top layer of timber from degrade by sun and rain.

In building the stack, layers of timber are separated by seasoned spacers [called stickers] spaced at intervals usually 450mm apart. The stickers are kept one above the other to prevent sagging of the timber. There is a balance in the spacing of the stickers, insufficient can allow sagging between the stickers but too many stickers slow the drying. Stickers are usually 19mm thick. The moisture content of the stack is checked at regular intervals until the desired moisture level is reached [normally in the 10% to 15% range.] Good practice requires a moisture meter to be used for checking moisture contents during the process.

Timber Stack for Drying

Timber processors involved in drying timber particularly those using kilns have usually developed schedules covering stack design for different thicknesses and species.

NOTE: The principles used in large scale commercial air drying can be used by timber enthusiasts wishing to dry specialized timbers but access to a moisture meter is helpful in monitoring the drying process. The section on turning in chapter 8 also makes mention on using air drying for seasoning by timber enthusiasts particularly for species normally only available in the unseasoned state.

Kiln Drying Process

To speed up the seasoning process and eliminate the weather variability factor the more efficient method of drying in a kiln is now widely used. As with air drying the building of a stack is still required to get air flow through and over the timber to be dried. The process involves the use of fans to move the air. As drying proceeds the moisture content of the air is progressively reduced. The procedure of progressively reducing the moisture content of the air being circulated minimizes reduces the possibility of twisting and warping of the timber if wet boards were immediately subject to completely dry heated air.

Schedules have been developed over the years for different timbers and sizes covering the stack required, air flows, temperatures and moisture contents to give the best kiln operation. With some timbers weights are placed on the tops of the stacks to prevent distortion as the drying proceeds.

Once the desired moisture content is reached it is normal to recondition the timber by blowing live steam through the stack. This ensures even moisture content through each piece of timber and reduces the possibility of stresses in the timber which can lead to distortion after the timber has left the kiln.

More modern developments now involve automatic control of the kiln with computers instead of manual control. The kiln drying program according to what timber is in the kiln is held by the computer which then automatically controls the whole operation. Some kilns are also using solar as the source of power during daylight hours.

The Choice between Unseasoned and Seasoned Timber

When undertaking any timber project the situation occurs as to whether unseasoned or seasoned timber should be used and a choice has to be made. In larger projects both options can frequently find an application. In others such as internal flooring, paneling and joinery, seasoned timber is the only logical option. A quick check on the advantages of each of the two options follows.

Unseasoned Timber
- Lower cost
- Can be used in exterior situations such as fencing and landscaping where the extra cost of seasoned timber serves no useful purpose.
- It is available in a more extensive range of larger sizes.
- It is the only suitable option for power poles, posts and other very large section applications unless a glue laminated product is specified.

Of course, unseasoned timber does have the disadvantages of shrinkage and can be prone to splitting, twisting and warping as it seasons.

Seasoned Timber
- It is a dimensionally stable product not subject to the shrinkage and splitting and twisting that can occur with unseasoned timber.
- Particularly with hardwoods the timber is lighter and easier to handle.
- Seasoning improves the strength and stiffness characteristics.
- Painting and finishing are improved.

Note: Even seasoned timber will expand and contract a little in interior situations as atmospheric moisture conditions change with changes in weather conditions.

While at times it is necessary to use the above criteria to make the correct choice much of the time this automatically happens in line with usual practice.

The Grading of Timber and Standards Involved

Introduction

The setting up of specifications and codes as it applies to most human activities has been around for centuries and it is no different today. It would not be difficult to imagine that even the ancient Egyptians prepared specifications for building the pyramids. In the building industry there are a large number of specifications and codes applying to the products used and also their method of use. As happens with other building materials such as plaster, metals and paint the timber industry refer to these specifications as standards.

These can apply to the building design and construction phase or to the products themselves. This chapter primarily deals with timber itself but some reference is made of a few construction standards.

The authority in Australia responsible for drawing up these standards is the Standards Association of Australia and standards are given an AS number. They have been prepared by suitably qualified people from within the timber industry and other bodies such as the Housing Industry, the CSIRO and State Forestry Departments working as committees under the supervision of Standards Australia staff. From time to time as the need arises the standards are updated. Where the need for a new standard is necessary this is also carried out.

Over the years there has been a lot of effort put into grouping a lot of the former standards into one more comprehensive and updated standard. However many of these former standards still exist and are listed on the Standards website along with the updated more comprehensive standard.

Design and Construction Standards

On the subject of design and building construction there are a number of important timber standards and the more important ones are given in the complete listing that follows. One of the most widely used is AS 1684 – Residential Timber Framed Construction. This sets out:

- The timber sizes required for all the elements involved in residential construction such as subfloor, wall and roof framing etc.
- It includes different tables for building in different wind speed areas around Australia including cyclonic areas.
- Separate tables exist for the different grades available both in pine and hardwood. The grades which are set out as stress grades [F ratings] have been derived by the visual grading method in accordance with the applicable standards. Explanation of F ratings is covered further on in this chapter.

As there is a large quantity of pine timber graded to MGP ratings there are separate supplements in to AS 1684 covering the MGP grades. While the AS 1684 standard is very comprehensive, covering both sizing, interpreting and design limitations, it is preferable that those desiring to use this valuable standard attend a training session on the subject to prevent misinterpretation.

Basic Timber Standards

Within the standards relating to timber, it can be considered that there are four standards in particular that have absorbed a large number of older standards. These four Australian Standards are as follows

- AS 2082 – Hardwood Visually stress graded for structural purposes
- AS 2858 – Softwood Visually stress graded for structural purposes
- AS 2796 – Hardwoods Sawn and Milled Products
- AS 4785 – Softwoods Sawn and Milled Products

These are widely used, and what each standard covers is detailed below. While AS2858 is the basic reference standard much of the construction grade timber is graded in some mills using advanced optical technique as the method of grading. This was explained in Chapter 2, on timber mill operations. A brief listing of some of the previous standards that have been incorporated into each of the above four has also been included.

IMPORTANT: The reader should be aware where grading is carried out at the source of production these graders have been specially trained in the interpretation of the grading rules.

The purpose of giving a brief explanation of the grading rules to the reader is to show the kinds of factors that have to be considered in the grading process. While errors can obviously occur, querying the grade supplied from a mill has to be approached cautiously. One of the regular complaints that happens, particularly with flooring, is that select grade is occasionally considered by some end users as being defect free wood and this is incorrect.

AS 2082 – Hardwoods

This standard covers the visual stress grading of sawn hardwood both in the unseasoned and seasoned state. It applies to all Australian hardwood species plus a wide range of imported hardwood timbers. It sets out four structural grades [1, 2, 3 and 4] plus an appearance grade. The appearance grade tightens the limits on items involved in each of the structural grades where a good appearance is required. However, it does not specify that the timber be clear i.e., free of any defects.

The purpose of grading is to limit the various factors that can affect the strength and in turn the stress rating of hardwood as compared to a defect free perfectly straight piece of timber. However, there is a range of grades so that maximum utilisation of the timber from the tree can be achieved. By referring to the table covering the basic strength of the individual species involved and the applicable structural grade established for the piece of timber a stress grade can be determined. Information on how this is done is part of the standard.

This stress grade can then be used as a basis for determining sizes required for the various building elements such as bearers, joists, beams and rafters etc. These were explained in the section on AS 1684 above.

Each of the structural grades and the appearance grade has maximum limits on the size and extent of defects that can naturally occur such as knots, holes, gum veins, gum pockets, splits and checks. Other controls include slope of grain, spring, bow and twist and of course a sawing tolerance. If there is timber missing on the edge called want and wane then where this occurs it has to comply with the limits allowed in the standard. The standard gives comprehensive details of how all these various factors are to be measured.

Previous standards, which include AS 082, AS 083 and AS 1483, have been absorbed into this standard. However, AS 3818, which covers

31

a range of heavy engineering hardwoods such as wharf decking is still used for grading these products and not AS 2082.

AS 2858 – Softwoods

This standard covers the visual stress grading of softwoods both in the unseasoned and seasoned state. It covers the Australian *pinus* species, hoop pine and cypress pine. It also includes a wide range of imported softwoods such as western red cedar, Douglas fir, Californian redwood, the spruces, firs and hemlock plus the many variety of pine from America and Europe.

However, a large proportion of the seasoned Australian *pinus* species such as radiata, slash and Caribbean required for structural purposes are not visually graded by using AS 2858 but are mechanically stress graded through a stress grader or optically graded automatically. While this is a much quicker and more economical method AS 2858 is still a valuable reference.

The standard AS 2858 sets out 5 structural grades [1, 2, 3, 4 and 5] plus a heart in stud grade [pinus only] and structural appearance grades. In the case of hoop pine which is covered separately there are three Stress grades F 5, F7 and F8 plus the respective appearance grades. With cypress pine which is also covered separately there are three Stress grades F4, F5 and F7 plus the appearance grades. As both hoop and cypress are single species it is possible to convert the grades straight into stress grades.

As occurs in hardwood grading those factors which reduce the strength of the timber are identified and a limit placed on each according to the structural grade involved. The main criteria are knots, holes. resin pockets, splits, decay, want and wane. The other factors which reduce strength such as slope of grain, variation from correct size are also covered. The purpose of having a number of structural grades in the standard is to ensure full utilization of the timber being milled. As is logical in the standards specifying sizes to be used in different situations particularly in residential construction such as AS 1684 sizes vary according to grade. Lower stress grades require larger sizes than the higher stress grades. However, the lower cost of the lower stress grades can often justify their use even though a larger size may be required.

AS 2796 – Seasoned Hardwood

In contrast to unseasoned hardwood standard because of a different application the standard for sawn and milled hardwood products AS 2796 has a different set of criteria in its grading rules. This standard covers flooring, decking, joinery timbers etc., and the grades are:

- Select grade
- Medium Feature grade [standard grade]
- High Feature grade
- Plus a parquetry grade which is a variation on select grade.

As well as having set limits on natural characteristics such as knots, gum veins gum pockets, checks etc., there are tight specifications on the quality of machining. Another feature is a difference in grading specifications for the face and the back of the timber.

The standard covers the following hardwood products – flooring, parquet flooring, light decking, cladding, internal lining, fascia, furniture components and feedstock for milling. It is divided into three sections

- 2796.1 – Product descriptions
- 2796.2 – Grade descriptions which covers the grading
- 2796.3 – Timber for furniture components.

This standard does not cover approved methods of fixing and finishing.

AS 4785 – Sawn Seasoned Softwoods

This standard is similar to AS 2796 but covers softwoods instead of hardwoods. It covers a range of previous individual standards which have been incorporated into one overall standard. This included standards which previously existed for products such as flooring, light decking, preservative treated cladding, fascia boards, internal lining and panelling, internal mouldings, joinery timbers and shelving. There are five grades defined under the grading rules:

- Clear grade
- Appearance grade
- Select grade
- Standard grade
- Utility grade

The principal difference between the clear and appearance grades is the complete exclusion of any holes in the clear grade regardless of their size.

There are three sections:

- AS 4785.1 – Product Description
- AS 4785.2 – Grade Description which covers the grading
- AS 4785.3 – Timber for furniture components.

The species covered include all Australian grown *pinus* species including radiata, Caribbean and slash plus imported species such as Douglas fir, western red cedar, Californian redwood and other American softwood species. It encompasses a number of previous standards 1489 to 1498, 1781 to 1787 and 2440 Douglas fir. However, cypress pine is still covered by AS 1810.

As is the case with AS 2796 the hardwood standard. this standard does not cover the approved methods of fixing and finishing the various products.

Benefits of Standards and Grading Rules

Some of the more important reasons are as follows.

- Timber is put on a recognised quality and performance basis developed by experts in the field in conjunction with Government authorities and members of the building and construction industries.
- Manufacturers, suppliers, builders, designers and users all then work to the same standard. This then prevents any arguments between parties involved if any problems arise. It also serves as a basis if any court actions occur.
- The grades have also been designed to include lower grades so that their use is possible and most efficient utilisation of the Australian timber resource is achieved.

Methods of Grading

Grading is carried out either visually, by mechanical stress grading or in some large up to date plants by optical scanning with a computer.

In visual grading this is done as the timber comes along from either the saw or the milling machine. This requires the grader to be thoroughly trained and familiar with the applicable grading standards. Because of the difficulty with manual grading with a complexity of knots, slope of grain, resin streaks and other characteristics of the *pinus* range, mechanical stress graders were developed in Australia many years ago and measure the strength at regular intervals [600mm] along the piece of timber by passing it between preset rollers and measuring the deflection. The roller pressures are preset to cover the dimensions and species of pine being processed. At each point of testing the deflection is measured, relayed to the computer which assesses from the greatest deflection found and marks each piece at the end with the relevant grade.

The calibration of the machine is carried out in accordance with an Australian Standard. Measurement of deflections under increasing load is measured by individually testing a large number of samples. To get the best possible consistency samples are taken for different species and different forest areas as conditions of growth affect strength which can also vary from tree to tree.

As discussed in Chapter 2 about saw milling operations, highly sophisticated grading is carried out in many very modern softwood sawmills. This involves optically scanning the timber as it passes along which is then continually referred to the grading rules in the associated computer and then each piece stamped with the lowest grade found.

The basis of the grading rules as set out depends on regular strength testing of large numbers of samples of the various species from the different forests around Australia.

List of Australian Standards for Timber

There is a very extensive list of specifications and the following list gives the more common standards as published by the Australian Standards Association and which can be purchased from them. The full list is available on their web site covering all kinds of timbers and their applications even down to wooden baby's cots. Here is a list of the more common ones used in the timber industry. A few go back very many years and most have been incorporated into larger standards covering a bigger range of species. For ease of reference the standards have been grouped into a number of general applications rather than being listed numerically

Standard Application

Design and Construction

- AS/NZS 1170 Structural design actions – Permanent, imposed and other actions
- AS/NZS 1170.2 Structural design actions – Wind actions
- AS 4055 Wind loads for housing
- AS/NZS 1328 Glue laminated structural lumber – Performance requirements
- AS 1530.7 Early Fire Hazard Properties of timber
- AS/NZS 1530.7 Methods of fire tests on materials, components, structures
- AS1684 Parts 1 to 4 – Guidelines and tables giving sizes for different stress grades for residential timber framed construction In both cyclonic and non-cyclonic areas
- AS 1684 Supplement Covers MGP Grades
- AS 1720.1 Timber Design and Construction Methods
- AS 1720.2 Timber Design – Timber properties
- AS 1720 4 Fire resistance of timber elements
- AS 1748 Machine Stress Grading of timber
- AS 2878 Strength Grouping of timbers
- AS/NZS 3837 Methods of test for heat and smoke release rates
- AS 4063 [1-3] Engineered Wood Products Testing and Values
- AS 4440 Installation of timber roof trusses

- AS/NZS 4557 Laminated Veneer Lumber [LVL] Determination of properties
- AS 5604 Timber Natural Durability Ratings

Timber and Grades

- AS 1080 Method of Test Slope of grain
- AS 1328 Glue Laminated Timber
- AS 1261 Parquetry Specification and Laying
- AS 1729 Wooden Tool Handles
- AS 1810 Cypress Pine Flooring and milled products
- AS 2082 Hardwood Visually Graded
- AS 2209 Poles for overhead lines
- AS 2796.2 Hardwood – Sawn and Milled Timber Grade descriptions
- AS 2858 Softwood – visually stress graded for structural purposes
- AS 3818.4 Cross Arms
- AS 3818.5 Mine Shaft Timbers
- AS 3818.6 Decking for wharves
- AS 3818.7 Large section sawn timber
- AS 3818.8 Stumps and Sole Plates
- AS 3818.9 Round treated hardwood corbels, girders and stringers
- AS 3818.10 Poles
- AS 4785 Timber Softwood Sawn and Milled Products
- BS EN 2015 16351 Cross Laminated Timber

Forest and Wood Products Australia (FWPA) Interim Structural and decorative

Board Products

- AS/NZS 1859 1-4 Reconstituted Wood Products Particle Board & Fibreboard
- AS/NZS 1860 Particleboard Flooring
- AS/NZS 2098 Plywood and Veneer Methods of test
- AS/NZS 2269 Plywood – Structural
- AS/NZS 2270 Plywood and Blockboard for internal use
- AS/NZS 2271 Plywood and Blockboard for exterior use
- AS/NZS 2272 Marine Plywood
- AS/NZS 4357 Hardboard
- AS 6669   Plywood Formwork

Engineered Timber Products

- AS 4063 Timber – stress graded – In-grade strength and stiffness evaluation

Other Timber Standards

- AS 1080 Methods of Test for Moisture Content
- AS /NZS1604.1 Preservative-treated wood-based products, Part 1: Products and treament
- AS 1613 Colours for marking stress grades
- AS 2688 Timber Doors
- AS 2689 Timber Door Sets
- AS 3660 Termite Management

NOTE: Standards are available from the Standards Association of Australia. To procure copies, contact the Standards Association of Australia, 16-20 Bridge Street, Sydney, NSW.

Comments on Timber Standards Listing

- As pointed out previously the above listing is only a selection of more commonly used timber standards. Others also exist.
- Australian standards are being regularly updated even though most have been in use for many years. However, it is still advisable to check beforehand if a reference needs to be made.
- The listing is for general information. Care has to be taken in studying standards as the correct interpretation of the various clauses is very important. Those using standards in grading of timber at the timber mills and other manufacturing plants are specially trained in their application.

Chapter 4: The Structure of Timber

Introduction

The purpose of this chapter is to give the readers an understanding of the structure of timber and the different types of cells involved. In so doing what is a softwood and what is a hardwood will be covered. Also covered will be an explanation of the essential differences between truewood [heartwood] and sapwood. The basis of it all is the microscopic cells which are the essential building blocks and how they go together will be explained.

In Chapter 1 on trees an attempt was made to explain the processes involved in the growth of a tree in very simple terms even though the processes are incredibly complex. In particular the way in which cells which make up the structure of timber are formed was explained. This chapter presented some interesting background general knowledge. With this in mind it is realized that in describing timber structure there is a need to repeat some of the information that was previously covered. One of these involved looking at a diagram of a typical cross section through the trunk of a tree. To save having to refer back to the trees chapter this drawing of a cross section is again illustrated below.

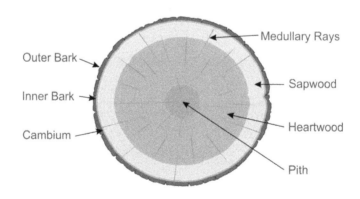

Tree Cross-section

Structure

Commercial timber is primarily sourced from the trunk of the tree. As also exists in branches, roots and other woody parts of the tree, the trunk is composed of a complex of interconnected cells. These cells are primarily aligned along the length of the trunk and the branches. There are also cells called rays at right angles to the length running from the outer surface of the trunk and the branches to the centre. The rays frequently can give a distinctive appearance to the timber after it has been milled and can be easily seen in silky oak.

The Cells

The cells are microscopic in size and cannot be even superficially examined without at least a magnification of ten. However, to properly examine the cell structure a much higher magnification [for example 500] is frequently used. To put this into perspective if we look at the common cells in softwoods under this higher magnification the cell diameter is still only 10mm across. To really examine some cells a high-powered electron microscope is needed. This particularly applies to smaller cells in the leaves and other smaller cells in the various plants. In short timber is made up of millions of cells that cannot be examined with the naked eye.

Growth of Cells

As the tree grows the diameter expands by the addition of further layers of cells

These cells are initially small and have very flexible walls [the primary walls] and this allows the cell to expand until reaches its full size. At this point two things occur firstly the primary walls are replaced by stiff secondary walls and a new layer of small cells are laid down again on the outer surface under the bark. This all occurs in the layer known as the cambium layer immediately under the bark. The result of this is that the mature cells then play no further role in increasing the diameter of the tree but are still involved in the movement of nutrients up and down the tree. A similar process occurs in the enlargement of the root structure. This is a critical area [as explained in Chapter 1] where moisture, nutrients and other elements involved in the cell process such as nitrogen, phosphorous, potassium, etc., are taken up from the soil. The increase in length of the trunk of the tree and the branches takes under the crown of the tree and at the ends of the branches where nutrients from photosynthesis in the leaves combine with nutrients brought up from the roots to form new cells and the topmost shoots extend the length of the trunk and the branches.

Another development is that as the tree grows the inner layers of mature cells become filled with resins, gums and a range of other substances and in so doing become blocked. These layers of cells then can no longer take part in the movement of nutrients up and down the trunk. This then gives rise to the terms sapwood which are the outer layers where nutrient movement is still occurring and truewood [heartwood] where the cells are blocked.

The significance of the above as regards truewood and sapwood is important to the timber designer or user. What it means is that as the sapwood and truewood consist of the same type of mature cells there is no difference in strength between sapwood and truewood. However, in a piece of timber the fact that in the tree the nutrients could move up and down in the sapwood also means that chemicals can be pumped in to the sapwood for preservative treatment. On the other hand, because the cells are blocked in the truewood, such treatment is normally not possible. While the sapwood has to remain free of blockages to allow transmission of nutrients up and down the tree some starch frequently can be found in this sapwood zone. As such it is a component in the process of building cells.

However, after the timber has been milled the presence of starch in the sapwood of some hardwood species can be attractive to borers. On the other hand, presence of various substances that are blocking the cells in truewood can be beneficial as it can confer resistance to fungal and insect degradation. This varies according to the species involved and relates to the substance blocking the cells in the truewood. As an example, the substances in the truewood of Australian cypress pine give it great durability against decay whereas the sapwood where there are no substances present is not durable and readily decays given the right conditions.

Different types of cells

There are four different types of cells in the timber in the trunk

- Vessels or Pores
- Tracheids
- Parenchyma Cells
- Fibres

The Vessels or Pores

These are the main structural elements of the hardwoods with an outer wall enclosing an inner space. At their ends they are perforated so that fluids can move up and down the tree via the cells. They also have pits on the sides that allow more interchange of fluids from cell to cell. The term pored timbers [hardwoods] and non-pored timbers [softwoods] is often used to distinguish between the two main types of timber [hardwoods and softwoods].

Tracheids

These are the main structural elements of the softwoods [conifers.] In shape they consist of structural tubes with round or pointed ends with their length aligned along the length of the tree trunk. Unlike the vessels which can vary in diameter, tracheids are relatively uniform in size. However, tracheids as a whole in the early wood [the spring growth] are usually larger than latewood [autumn and winter growth]. This can be seen in the photos shown on the next page. Like the vessels the tracheids are able to conduct fluids up and down the trunk so long as they have not become blocked typically with gums and resins. In the softwood cell photo the difference in size of the tracheids between early wood and the smaller latewood is very apparent. The differences in size of the vessels [pores] in the hardwood are also easy to see. The upper photo shows the tracheids in conifers, the lower pores in a hardwood timber. The photos were taken from a Queensland Forestry Department brochure.

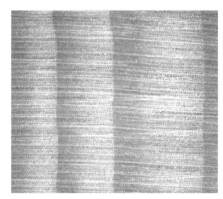 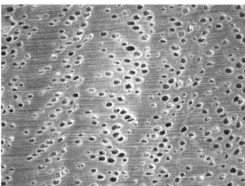

Tracheids in a Conifer   Pores in a Hardwood Timber

Parenchyma cells

These cells are scattered through both hardwoods and softwoods and served as areas of food storage in the tree. Cells are usually brick shaped in appearance when viewed under high magnification. Cell walls are thinner and allow nutrients to move through. Unlike vessels and tracheids, they contribute very little to the structural strength of the tree and timber. However, in identification of the various species under magnification they are often very useful.

Fibres

Fibres are the final series of cells that go to make up the structure of the tree. They play no part in the transmission of fluids and nutrients but serve to provide extra structural support. Fibres resemble tracheids in appearance being long tubes with pointed ends. They only occur in hardwoods and not in softwoods and do not transmit fluids.

Hardwoods and Softwoods

As mentioned above hardwoods which belong to the botanical group angiosperms have a different cell structure to the softwoods such as the pines, spruces and firs which belong to the class gymnosperms. In the hardwoods the cell sizes vary from small to large whereas in the softwoods as pointed out above they are relatively uniform in size. Cell sizes also vary according to the seasons. As was shown in the previous photo of cells taken with high magnification cells are a little larger in terms of size in the periods of rapid growth viz. spring and early summer. The term softwood is a botanical one and does not refer to the hardness of the timber. For example balsa is extremely soft but is classed as a hardwood botanically because of its cell structure.

Having a reasonable knowledge of the cell structure of timber does give the user a better understanding of the properties of timber especially timber's movement with changes in moisture content, the ability to pressure treat with preservatives and susceptibility to degrade in service.

Timber Identification

Under magnification each timber species has its own 'fingerprint' which is related to its cell structure. Identification of species then involves looking at the sample under magnification and comparing with cell structure photographs where the species has previously been identified by using external factors such as appearance of the tree, the leaf shape, the bark, flowers and fruit, etc. The experts involved in identifying the different timber species using magnification need a good knowledge of cell structure. However as would be expected with the many thousands of species that exist worldwide this knowledge does not cover all world species. For example, Australian experts have no trouble identifying most Australian species but do have limitations in identifying the great number of imported species particularly those from the worlds rain forests. In the different areas of forest and where mills are established, staff normally build up knowledge about the local species being supplied for milling by the appearance of the logs and the bark.

Chemical Composition of the Cells

In the previous section the types of cells which make up timber were detailed and this covered both softwoods and hardwoods. A basic knowledge of what chemicals go to make up the timber cells, how this happens and their properties is very useful. This is because it makes it possible to understand the processes that are occurring in the growth of a tree. It also gives an idea of what foods are available in the timber and then are available as nutrients for fungi, termites and borers to digest.

Some simple chemistry might help. It is widely known that water is H2O which is made up of two atoms of hydrogen attached to one atom of oxygen to make the water molecule. A glass of water contains millions of molecules and this gives some concept of the minute size of a molecule.

Three main chemicals [molecules] make up the cell structure in timber. They are:

- Cellulose
- Hemicelluloses
- Lignin

These chemicals are also widespread in all plants. For example, cotton is practically composed of pure cellulose. As mentioned in the chapter on trees all are carbohydrates made up of large numbers of carbon, hydrogen and oxygen atoms. As is well known carbohydrates are better known as a constituent of many foods but obviously to be edible need to have a different arrangement of the carbon, hydrogen and oxygen atoms to the three chemicals above which are not edible for humans.

Cellulose

This is an organic chemical [a polysaccharide i.e., complex sugar] where the atoms – carbon [44%], oxygen [50%] and hydrogen [6%] – involved are joined up in long chains to form the molecule. Apart from being a major constituent of timber, cellulose also widely occurs as a common constituent of many other items of commerce. As mentioned above cotton is almost pure cellulose. Cellulose is also the basic raw material of the paper and pulp industry.

Hemicellulose

This is similar in composition to cellulose with carbon, hydrogen and oxygen atoms but the atoms instead of being stretched out as a long chain are arranged to be more compact. As a very rough analogy on a macro scale imagine cellulose as being a three meter long 150 wide board and, in comparison, hemicellulose a piece of plywood 900mm by 600mm. The hemicelluloses are gelatinous in nature without the stiffness of cellulose. They account for 30% of hardwoods and 20% of softwoods.

Lignins [derived from the Latin word for wood – *lignum*]

These are the third chemical involved in the four cell types. They are phenolic polymers composed again of carbon, hydrogen and oxygen atoms but the atoms are joined together in different ways. They function as a glue. In the cell itself the lignin functions to give it rigidity and in the wood it acts as a bonding agent between the cells to form a strong composite material. There is a slight difference in the chemical structure of the lignin in hardwoods to that in softwoods but it is still serving the purpose as a bonding agent in both. Dependent on speciesthey can account for up to 30% of the dry weight of timber. For the production of paper where cellulose is the majority component the lignin has to be removed and a number of processes exist to carry this out.

As pointed out above the main atoms involved are carbon, hydrogen and oxygen and these are sourced from the carbon dioxide in the surrounding air and water drawn from the ground by the roots and absorbed from moisture in the air.

Photosynthesis

The three molecules [organic chemicals] mentioned above are created by a process called photosynthesis. Photosynthesis, put simply, is the process by which light [solar energy] falling on the chlorophyll in the leaves is converted to chemical energy. The process is chemically extremely complicated. However, in so doing it converts carbon dioxide and water into the constituent chemicals used in producing the cells in the trees that become timber. The more intense the light the greater the rate of photosynthesis. Direct sunlight gives higher rates than in shady areas. However, photosynthesis still goes on in shady areas with many plants adapting to shade. The more intense sunlight in tropical areas means trees grow faster than in arctic areas. While photosynthesis is apparently very simple in concept the mechanism is exceedingly complex and only really understood by experts in the subject.

Cell Production

Conversion of these three main chemicals into the main cell types in trees then requires them to move up and down the tree and be available for cell production. This can be for producing the leaves, or increasing the length of the trunk and branches, increasing the diameter of the trunk or producing the roots themselves. It also involves many other chemical compounds. The process involved in conversion into nutrients and then into cells is incredibly complicated chemically. An essential molecule for photosynthesis happening in the leaves is the chemical chlorophyll. Many of the elements involved in the photosynthesis process in the leaves have to drawn up from the ground through the roots. Similarly, elements involved required in this complex process of producing the various types of cells in various parts of the tree are also drawn up through the roots.

The process on how moisture and nutrients are drawn up against the forces of gravity is also complicated.

Summary

In summary in very simple terms the situation is as follows:

- The chemicals involved have been derived from carbon dioxide in the atmosphere and water from the air and the ground and in this process some oxygen is released into the air. Other trace chemicals are extracted from the ground by the roots.
- The three chemicals listed above viz cellulose, hemicelluloses and lignin are combined in different ways to make up the four types of cells – vessels, tracheids, parenchyma and fibres. The processes involved are incredibly complex and many other chemicals are also involved in the processes.
- The cellulose gives the cell its structural strength, but the hemicelluloses involved in the cell structure are gelatinous in nature.
- The lignins present play a vital role in the bonding the chemicals that make up the cell itself and also in bonding the cells together to produce the timber structure.
- The proportions of the three chemicals vary in percentage from species to species according to differences in cell structure. The proportions vary from
  - Cellulose – up to 50%
  - Hemicelluloses – 20% - 30%
  - Lignins – up to 30%
- The differences in cell structure are responsible for differences in properties of different species such as strength, hardness, density etc. Cell structure is thus extremely important.

Ecological Considerations

The availability of carbon dioxide in the surrounding air is essential for the growth of trees and plants. Trees undergoing rapid growth require more carbon, hydrogen and oxygen and so need more CO_2 whereas mature trees require less as they are not putting on the same amount of new growth. However, all trees contribute to CO_2 reduction as do the multitude of other plants that make up the plant kingdom such as the crops, grains and grasses. Obviously the greater the areas devoted to trees and plants the more CO_2 that can be absorbed but this is of course subject to prevailing climatic conditions. Areas that do not favour plant growth such as arid areas like deserts and frozen areas contribute little to CO_2 reduction. As timber is used in all types of construction the carbon content which was derived from atmospheric carbon dioxide is permanently locked away and is only released if the timber is used as a fuel when again the carbon is converted to carbon dioxide. In the forest the carbon is also locked away in the trees but the occurrence of bushfires does release the carbon back into the atmosphere as carbon dioxide.

Other Chemical Substances in the Cells

As well as the three main chemicals that comprise the basic cell structure there are a large number of chemicals that are found in the sap that is moving down from the crown and up from the roots. Of major importance are the special nutrients involved in the very complicated process of cell development whether it be the crown, roots or for increase in trunk length and diameter. These chemicals include:

- Starch, which is the reserve carbohydrate not only in trees but also in most plants. The presence of starch in the sapwood provides food for borers attacking timber such as lyctus [the powder post borer]. Again, the starch molecule is made up of carbon, hydrogen and oxygen but the atoms are joined together differently.

- Those chemicals that give different timbers their specific colours from black in ebony through a wide range of reds, browns, pinks, even to purples down to creamy colours in a lot of softwoods. These are generally concentrated in the truewood [heartwood] where they have collected. However, as the various chemicals are still moving up and down the sapwood collection in the sapwood cells would inhibit free movement. Consequently, while the colours of the heartwood in hardwoods can vary from species to species, the sapwood generally are similar. In the case of most of the pines because the timber is mostly sapwood the colours are creamy to light straw in colour. However not all softwoods are similar in colour to the pines as for example the American redwood. The organic chemicals that occur which provide the colouring matter in timber generally break down under the influence of direct sunlight. If not protected by clear finishes containing ultra violet screening chemicals the timber in time will assume a grey colour. Occasionally the chemicals may be inorganic rather than organic and these are more light-stable.

- Inorganic chemicals essential for cell production and in turn tree growth. Particularly important are compounds of nitrogen, phosphorus, potassium [NPK] plus smaller amounts of other chemicals such as magnesium, molybdenum, zinc, calcium etc. These are drawn up from the roots and are well known to the home gardener as elements in

commercial fertilisers.
- Silica taken up by some species such as turpentine, brushbox and walnut. When accumulated in the truewood, this provides a real deterrent for chewing insects such as marine borers, termites etc. Its presence of course makes sawing and machining more difficult as it blunts saws and woodworking machinery.
- Certain aromatic chemicals that give different species their individual odours, particularly when freshly sawn. They are found in the truewood and in some cases they also discourage attack by insects and fungi. Australian cypress pine is a good example of a timber where the heartwood contains chemicals that make it resistant to fungal attack.

As mentioned above, the inner cells of the trunk of the tree progressively become filled with gums, resins and most of the chemicals listed above. The wide variety of these substances may confer special properties to the truewood in which they accumulate. They may greatly increase resistance to fungal attack [rot and decay] and resistance to attack by insects. Only some of these chemicals and in particular starch are present in the sapwood which make the timber attractive to some insects.

Sapwood to Truewood Ratio

The percentage of sapwood to truewood decreases with increasing age of the tree. Young vigorously growing trees require a much wider sapwood band to ensure that an adequate supply of nutrients is moved up and down the tree. Older mature eucalypts with a diameter of 900mm or more may only have a sapwood band of 50mm. Because as mentioned above the colouring chemicals tend to lodge permanently in the truewood and not to be lodged in the sapwood the sapwood band is much lighter in colour and reflects more the natural colour of the basic cells. This in practice also makes it easier to determine if the sapwood in sawn or dressed timber has been preservative treated.

Beneficial Properties of the Chemicals Found in the Cells in Truewood

As mentioned above some of the chemicals that accumulate in the cell structure of the truewood [heartwood] in timber give the timber special properties.

Resistance to Decay

The presence in the truewood of substances that inhibit fungal growth and in turn decay will confer increased durability to timber. The presence, type and amount of such substances varies from species to species and so gives differences in durability. In hardwoods this can result in some species e.g., the ironbarks being extremely durable [Class 1], some are moderately durable [Class 2] and others for example Tasmanian oak have limited durability [Class 3] in exposed above ground and in inground situations.

Most pines are not durable because of the timber is mostly sapwood and there is an absence of the essential chemicals that confer durability. They are categorized as Class 4 the lowest of the durability resistance rating classes.

As the sapwood it has little or no extractives that repel fungi it readily rots or decays when exposed to external conditions. This applies regardless of the durability of the truewood. As an example, as mentioned above, grey ironbark is a Class 1 durability timber which means it is extremely durable when exposed to the conditions where fungal attack can take place [e.g., exterior weather exposure] but its sapwood quickly decays under such conditions. This is common with all hardwoods regardless of the durability class to which they belong. It is a common cause of problem in external construction if the timber contains sapwood that has not been preservative treated.

Resistance to Termites and Insects

In a similar fashion to resistance to fungi, certain extractives and mineral substances in the cells can confer resistance to termites and insects. Again, this varies from species to species. There is also a variability as to the resistance of the sapwood. While the sapwood of all species is not resistant to termites, only the sapwood of some timber species is attacked by the lyctus [powder post] borer, the criterion usually being the presence or absence of starch.

Effect on Density and Moisture Take Up

While the cell structure is the main factor, the presence of extractives obviously affects the density of timber. It also affects the ability to take up water. This is important in the timber preservation process where it is impractical to penetrate the truewood of hardwoods even under pressure and vacuum and only the sapwood zone can be treated. However, this does not apply to the penetration of atmospheric moisture which is in the gaseous phase and can be taken up in the cell walls. The subject of moisture and its relationship to timber is more fully explained in Chapter 6.

Chapter 5: Properties Of Timber

An understanding of the properties of timber as it applies to the various species allows the user to correctly specify the product to be used. Problems arise even with experienced professionals, because the properties required of the timber in a specific application may not be inherent in the species selected. An example is the misconception among some users that because it is a hardwood such as a species of eucalypt it will be durable in external situations. One timber that falls into this category is the very useful and popular Tasmanian Oak. However, it is rated Class 3 durability and therefore should not be used in fully exposed situations even though it is available as an F17 grade. In Chapter 11 a number of case histories are given for readers to explore how problems occurred through insufficient understanding of the properties of timber.

The more important properties that those using timber need to have a good basic understanding of are listed below. Each will be examined.

- Density
- Strength
- Hardness
- Toughness
- Appearance
- Timber's moisture content and reaction to moisture [Chapter 6]
- Durability [Chapter 7]
- Working Properties Sawing, Machining etc. [Chapter 8]

While there are possibly other properties that could be added, the above eight are an attempt to simplify the list and should cover most situations. Because the last three properties require detailed consideration, the three separate chapters [6, 7, and 8] that follow cover these subjects. Only the first five will be considered in this chapter.

Density

Density of timber in very simple terms refers to how heavy it is and is expressed as its weight in kilograms per cubic metre. Timber can range from very light such a balsa wood [*ochroma lagorus*] density 175kg/m3 to very heavy such as iron bark [density 1100 kg/m3 seasoned]. This variation impacts on all phases of timber operations from logging of the tree to the mill operations, movement through the milling processes, trucking of mill production and then down to timber's use in commerce whether it be in building construction or furniture manufacture or other uses. Apart from the weight situation and its implications, heavier and denser timbers are harder to process whether it be sawing, dressing or machining. As moisture is released from freshly sawn wood so the density drops and two different reference points are used viz the unseasoned or green off saw density and the seasoned density which is when the moisture content has been reduced to the range of 10% to 15% and 12% is quoted. The Appendix provides a list of the more common timbers with the properties of each and this includes density green and dry.

Strength

Obviously, a knowledge of the inherent strength of the various timber species is vital in the design of sizes required for different applications. Because the term strength is quite broad this has to be defined so the right data are used. Also, into this has to be integrated the timber grade which takes account of the natural features such as knots, gum veins and the slope of grain that will affect strength. Fortunately for the normal user and designer, timber tables have been prepared for a large range of applications setting out the sizes required for the different stress grades of timber. This saves the need to do the timber engineering calculations.

The two main terms used in the definition of strength are Modulus of Rupture [MOR] and Modulus of Elasticity [MOE]. Modulus of Rupture measures the load that has to be applied to cause the timber to break while Modulus of Elasticity measures the amount of deflection that occurs as increasing load is applied. Both are important and vary from species to species. All terms used in the definition of strength can be tied back to the cell structure of the timber species involved. These terms particularly apply when a load is applied that will cause the timber to bend or break. There are also other types of strength which are important viz. shear strength and crushing strength.

Shear Strength applies when forces or loads being applied cause the timber to shear i.e., be torn apart. Shear forces being applied at right angles to the length of the timber are always higher than that parallel to the length.

Compressive Strength or Crushing Strength is a measure of the resistance to loads or forces which are trying to reduce the timber member size. Take for example the situation where a timber joist is being supported by a bearer. At the point of support the timber bearer is tending to be crushed and needs to have sufficient compressive strength to prevent indentation.

Strength Grades

Based on extensive testing of a large number of samples an average figure has been allocated for a large number of the common species for each of the properties used to define the strength groups. Six strength groups

[S1 to S6] have been developed and in each the following properties have been defined. These are:

- Density [in kilograms per cubic metre of the oven dry timber]
- Modulus of Rupture [in megapascals]
- Modulus of Elasticity [in megapascals]
- Maximum Crushing Strength [in megapascals]
- Maximum Shear Strength [in megapascals]

A megapascal [MPa] is the metric unit of force acting on an area. It is the metric term that relates to the old Imperial pounds per square inch. One megapascal = approx. 145 pounds per sq. inch [psi] Just as psi was used in many different applications e.g., pressures of water, steam etc., so megapascals are similarly used in different applications. The other term related to the megapascal is the Newton [named after Sir Isaac Newton] and it is the force needed to accelerate one kilogram at a rate of one metre per second squared. It is widely used to cover the power of engines [motor vehicles]

Stress and Strain

Two terms that have been used for a very long time are stress and strain. When an external force [load] is applied to a timber member a measure of a particular timber's resistance to this force or load is known as its stress grade. Strain on the other hand is the change in shape or size that occurs. Some mistakenly believe the two terms are the same but this is not so.

Stress Grades

From the integration of timber grades with the strength groups the basic working stresses [stress grades] were derived. This then gave a practical basis for timber design. Obviously, for a particular species, a clear piece of timber is stronger than one with natural defects such as knots. The term F grade was adopted, and this then gives a meaningful grade to be used in the sizing of timber for different applications. The grades adopted were F43,34,27,22,17,14,11,8,7,5,4 with F43 being the strongest. Note: F43 is no longer included in contemporary standards.

Grading for Defects

As regards grading for natural defects, four grades are used in the various Australian Standards for hardwoods and softwoods. These are Structural grades 1 to 4 with 1 having the least defects and Structural grades SD 1 to 4 if the timber is seasoned.

The relevant Stress grade [F rating] is then derived from the two following tables, one for unseasoned timber, one for seasoned timber

[12% moisture content]. Thus, the two factors are taken into account in the following table viz the basic strength of the species and the timber grade involved.

Unseasoned Timber   STRESS GRADE

Grade as per relevant Aust. Standard	Relevant strength groups					
	S1	S2	S3	S4	S5	S6
Structural 1	F27	F22	F17	F14	F11	F8
Structural 2	F22	F17	F14	F11	F8	F7
Structural 3	F17	F14	F11	F8	F7	F5
Structural 4	F14	F11	F8	F7	F5	F4

The F rating relates to the strength in bending so that an F14 stress grade has a basic strength of 14 megapascals <u>in bending</u> and an F27 stress grade has a strength of 27 megapascals. This is a very useful and practical table for timber mills supplying into the building industry. If for example the mill is sawing a blackbutt log [a very common specie] and has an order to supply some unseasoned F17 timber it refers to the above table knowing that the strength group of blackbutt is S2 so it has to grade the timber to structural grade 2. However, if F14 grade was required then structural grade 3 would be sufficient. However, in practice the quality of the log might be such that the vast majority of the timber being sawn is structural grade 2 or better so that even though the order is for F14 the end user is actually getting mostly F17 or higher. This sometimes causes trouble on site, as many users understandably do not recognize that a higher stress grade has been supplied and want to reject the timber that is actually F14 as not being up to grade based on their comparison of the natural defects of the two grades supplied as F14.

Seasoned Timber

Grade as per Relevant Australian Standard	Stress Grade for relevant strength Groups					
	SD1	SD2	SD3	SD4	SD5	SD6
Structural 1	F34	F34	F27	F22	F17	F14
Structural 2	F34	F27	F22	F17	F14	F11
Structural 3	F27	F22	F17	F14	F11	F8
Structural 4	F22	F17	F14	F11	F8	F7

A comparison with the stress grades determined for unseasoned timber shows that seasoning timber results in a much higher stress grade For example a piece of grey ironbark which has a strength group of S1 or SD1 when graded to structural 1 gives an F27 stress grade in the unseasoned state and F34 if seasoned.

Mechanical Stress Grading

While the above method of arriving at a stress grade was and still is used, computer controlled automatic stress graders were developed by the CSIRO many years ago to provide a quicker way and overcome the problem that occurs in grading plantation pines where the assessment of large numbers of knots is time consuming and difficult by manual grading. The process involves the timber being continuously fed through the machine, and the deflection from a loaded moving roller against two opposing stationary rollers is measured at regular intervals along each piece. From the deflection readings taken, the computer takes the greatest deflection, converts it to the stress grade for the species and size being tested, and then marks the end of the piece with the calculated stress grade. This greatly speeds up the grading process.

Other Methods of Stress Grading

As pointed out under Mill Operations in Chapter 2, even more sophisticated methods of arriving at the stress grade for pine have been developed as timber proceeds along the production line. In this the timber is continuously optically scanned and the results fed into a computer where it is automatically checked with the grading rules for the species involved and the stress grade allocated. At the end, the piece is branded with the lowest stress grade found. This method is coming into increasing use in newer more modern pine processing plants.

MGP Grading

In addition to stress grades being labeled with an F rating many pine milling plants are instead now branding directly with an MGP [machine graded pine] rating in three grades MGP 10, 12 and 15 with of course 15 being the strongest. This grading was carried out after a development program and gives more and reliable data when used in the construction design tables.

Influence of Timber Dimensions on Load Carrying Capacity

There are three simple factors regarding timber dimension as to the load that can be carried by rectangular members.

- The load a timber member such as a beam can carry is directly proportional to the width, e.g., a 100mm wide beam will carry twice the load that can be carried by a 50mm wide beam, i.e., 100mm/ 50mm = 2
- The load that can be carried is proportional to the square of the depth, e.g., a 100mm deep beam will carry four times the load a 50mm deep beam will carry, i.e., 100mm/ 50mm = 2 squared = 4

- The bending strength of a timber member is inversely proportional to its span so that if the span is doubled the load that can be carried is reduced to half i.e., 1 divided by 2 = 0.5. Similarly, if the span is trebled the load is reduced to one third. Reducing the span similarly increases the bending strength by the same factors.

Two other factors are important.

- Firstly, if the load is uniformly distributed [i.e., spread over the length of the member] the load that can be carried is twice the load that can be carried if all of the load is being carried at one point. As an example, the weight of roofing material [tiles, corrugated iron, etc.] on a building can be considered to be spread across the total length of the roof batten between points of support on the rafter whereas the rafter is being loaded at points by the battens and not uniformly spread. The rafter can then be considered as carrying point loads. This will therefore affect the calculations of each of the members.
- Secondly, as regards deflection of a timber member, this is proportional to the cube of the span. For example, if the span is doubled the deflection is increased by 8 times, i.e., 2^3 [2 x 2 x 2] = 8
- While it is very useful to be aware of the foregoing points as regards strength of timber, in domestic dwelling calculations extensive construction tables covering all timber members from bearers, joists and posts to roof battens exist. However, the principles can be useful in the layout of such elements as bearers and joists in coming up with the most cost-effective solution. Knowing that increasing the depth of a member is more effective than increasing the width is helpful. In larger construction projects where it can be found the tables are not applicable the services of a suitably qualified person using timber engineering principles is required. However, the points are also useful for simple small furniture and cabinet work particularly where there is a mix of the need for adequate size plus aesthetics such as appearance, e.g., it may be better to increase the width or perhaps the depth of the member.
- Hardness is a measure of a species' ability to resist indentation. The hardness of timber is important in some applications but in many it is not considered important. As an example, the selection of a timber for flooring requires that it be hard enough to not easily be indented with high heels and easily damaged. Another example is the selection of species suitable for bowling alley flooring where the balls can cause damage and therefore very hard timbers are required. This is straight forward. On the other hand, the hardness of timbers used in domestic wall framing where it is covered could possibly not be considered a critical matter. However, hardness is also frequently associated with difficulty in sawing, planing and nailing so softer timbers are easier to use.
- Hardness is usually measured by the Janka hardness test, which measures the load required to press a 11mm steel ball into the surface to half its depth. The hardness of timber is lower in the unseasoned state

but it is normal for the Janka test to be carried out on seasoned timber because applications where hardness is important normally require the use of seasoned timber. Janka hardness can vary from 3 to 4 for typical pine species used in construction to over 16 for grey ironbark. A listing of the hardness of a number of Australian species is set out in the Appendix section at the end of the book.

- Toughness is usually defined by timber's ability to resist shocks and blows, in other words its impact strength. A typical use that requires high toughness is handles used in axes and hammers of various kinds. Many properties of timber are involved in assessing toughness including resistance to splitting, grading for defects, modulus of rupture and modulus of elasticity. Some species such as spotted gum and hickory are very tough but have to meet at least number one grade in the grading rules as obviously natural defects such as knots and gum veins and slope of grain can seriously affect toughness.

- As mentioned above, toughness also can be looked on in another way in its ability to resist splitting under bending and impact conditions. A frequently quoted example of this is with timber diving boards where in addition to having adequate bending strength and resistance to snapping the board must also resist splitting when under load.

- Appearance. In many applications the appearance of the finished timber is what determines what species will be used. However, this does not apply, of course, if the timber is to be painted. Also, in structural applications appearance is not important except where occasionally the building design may call for the timber to be clear finished such as exposed beams and rafters. This section on appearance does not cover the differences between sawn and dressed timber or where the surface has been specially machined as for example rougher headed decking or surface treatment of some types of exterior cladding.

The most common applications where appearance is paramount are in flooring and internal paneling in buildings, in furniture and in veneered work.

There are a number of separate factors which contribute to timber's appearance, viz, Colour, Grain, Texture and Figure.

Colour

The colour in timber is derived from various substances [primarily organic] which in hardwoods are chiefly laid down in the cells in the truewood with very little in the sapwood. The natural colours are highly prized and may vary from off whites through tans, shades of browns and pink and red to black as in ebony. Of course, the eventual colour of the finished article can be changed by application of stains but this requires care as not all timbers will stain evenly and a blotchy finish can result. When selecting the type of clear finish to be applied solvent based finishes tend to enhance the natural colour while the water based clear finishes have minimal effect on what is the natural colour.

Exposure of the timber to sunlight eventually causes the colour to bleach resulting in a grey colour. This is caused by breakdown of the organic chemicals giving the original colour whether they be in the timber itself or in an applied stain. On the other hand, if the pigment is an inorganic substance, for example titanium dioxide [white] or carbon [black] then reasonable resistance to colour change from the sunlight can be expected. Unfortunately, however, not all inorganic pigments are light stable.

Grain, Texture and Figure

The definition of these elements in the appearance of timber are not clear to many wood users and frequently incorrectly used. The British standards and definitions by authorities such as the CSIRO are roughly the same and are used as a basis in the following explanations.

Grain

Grain is usually taken to mean the general direction of the fibres and cell structure. So in a straight grained piece of timber the direction is in general parallel to the main axis [length] of the piece of timber or trunk of the original tree. As seen in the chapter on grading grain direction is very important in strength considerations and 'slope of grain' is the term used in the grading rules. Where the angle of the grain is considerably different to being parallel to the length it is frequently referred to as being 'crossgrained'. The term 'interlocked' grain is often encountered and means that the adjacent layers of the wood are spirally inclined to each other. Such timbers are frequently difficult to work. 'Wavy Grain' is often encountered and instead of the general direction of the grain being continuously straight waves along the length. One of the causes for this is the occurrence of branches along the trunk of the tree. This type of grain can be very decorative.

In the case of decorative veneers while the direction of the grain does affect the appearance it is generally not a major consideration. However, in veneers being produced for manufacture of structural plywoods, the grain direction is very important for strength reasons particularly with the face and back, i.e., the surface veneers.

Texture

Texture refers to the size and distribution of the timber cells even though the individual cells are only visible under magnification. So in timbers that are fine textured the cells that make up the timber are small, others where vessels [pores] in hardwood occur can be medium and some coarse in appearance. Some examples are for fine texture many of the beech species, for medium texture blackbutt and white stringybark and for coarse texture tallowwood and red mahogany. Uneven texture can also occur along a piece of timber where growth of the tree is more vigorous and cells are larger according to variations in climatic conditions. Frequently timbers are referred to as fine, medium or coarse 'grained' when the correct description refers to the texture not the grain.

Figure

Figure refers to the ornamental markings present on the surface formed by variations in cell structure. It is very dependent on whether the timber was back cut or quarter cut and in the case of veneers the angle of slicing of the solid timber billet. The figure shown by different timbers is highly prized in furniture and other internal decorative applications. Some examples of different figures are shown in the photographs on the next page. The effects also reflect in part the influence of the texture and grain.

Figure 1 shows the figure in rotary peeled alpine ash due to the arrangement of the pores. Figure 2 shows fiddleback in Tasmanian blackwood.

Figure 3 shows the well-known flakey figure on the quarter cut face of silky oak due to large medullary rays.

Figure 4 shows a less prominent flakey figure on the quarter cut face of North Queensland red tulip oak.

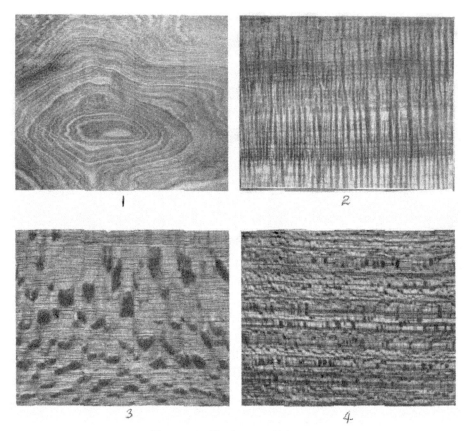

Figures in Timber and Veneer

Chapter 6: Timber And Moisture

Introduction

In the previous chapter, five of the properties of timber that the user and designer need to thoroughly understand were listed and explained in detail. These were density, strength, hardness, toughness and appearance. Chapter 6 is a very important chapter and explains how closely timber and moisture are related. Its importance cannot be overemphasized and many of the problems that occur in construction can be linked back to not understanding this relationship. This impacts not only in the production of timber products but particularly in the great variety of construction processes. Many of the basic concepts involved in understanding timber and moisture are linked in to the cell structure and this will also be explained. Some aspects of timber and moisture were covered briefly in Chapter 3 in the section on seasoning.

Of basic importance is the fact that timber will expand and contract as its moisture content increases and decreases. This is very apparent when doors, drawers and other items in the house may become difficult to open and close during periods of wet weather. Allowance for this movement has to be made during the building of houses, the construction of furniture and in other timber uses. Typical examples where allowing for this movement is essential include the laying of timber floors, the laying of decking timbers and allowance for shrinkage where unseasoned timber is used in domestic construction.

This movement in the case of timber with change in moisture content is entirely different what happens with metals. Metals expand and contract with changes in temperature of the surrounding environment. In addition, the per cent change is the same in all directions –length, breadth and width. However, the coefficient of linear expansion which is the determinant used is small so that with changes in atmospheric temperature from very hot to very cold causes little movement to occur. This then does not cause problems with items fabricated from metal such as steel beams and aluminum windows. However, problems can occur if the metal is exposed to very high temperatures as can occur in the case of fire. For example, if steel beams are being used to support floors or roof structures the expansion can push over external walls causing the whole of the supported structure to fall in. There is a famous historical case where this occurred in a large manufacturing plant with disastrous consequences.

The situation with timber as regards temperature is different. The range in atmospheric temperatures by itself has no effect on the dimensions of timber. However, in situations where timber is being exposed to higher atmospheric temperatures it can then cause the moisture content of the timber to be reduced and then reduction in dimensions occurs. An example of this is flooring subject to sun through windows. Continued expansion of metals to wet conditions of course requires that protective measures against corrosion are required. Where steel and timber are being used in close contact changes in the dimensions in width and depth of the timber with changes in moisture have to be taken into consideration. As can be seen from the above the implications of change in dimension with changes in moisture content of timber are vitally important in the design process.

The subjects to be covered in this chapter are:

- Definition of Moisture Content and Methods of Testing
- Moisture in timber and Fibre Saturation Point [FSP]
- Timber Movement in different directions – Length, Tangential and Radial
- The Shrinkage of Unseasoned Timber
- Heart in timber
- The term Unit Shrinkage
- Movement of Seasoned Timber
- Timber and the Atmosphere – Equilibrium Moisture Content [EMC]

The various uses of seasoned and unseasoned timber, the benefits that each can bring and reasons why was already explained in Chapter 3 on seasoning.

Before considering the subjects above there is one important point to be considered. This is that timber is a hygroscopic material which simply means that it will either take in moisture or alternatively give off moisture as it comes into equilibrium with the moisture content of the surrounding atmosphere. It is not unique in this property. If it has been freshly milled with a moisture content well above that in the surrounding atmosphere it will give off moisture and eventually shrink in size. Once it has come into equilibrium with the moisture content in the surrounding air, changes that occur in the moisture content of the surrounding air will still result in changes in the moisture content of the timber i.e., timber will increase in size with increase in moisture content or shrink in size when losing moisture. While the application of coatings such as paints and other finishes will slow the movement of moisture in and out of the timber it will not stop it happening. This is easily seen in solid timber strip flooring where the individual boards will still expand and contract with changes in the moisture content of the surrounding atmosphere even though they are coated with several coats of polyurethane finish. The moisture slowly goes through the finish in the vapour form.

Definition of Moisture Content and Methods of Testing

This definition was also previously set out in Chapter 3 which covered seasoning and grading of timber. The percent moisture content is defined as the weight of water contained in a piece of timber compared to the weight of the wood substance itself expressed as a percentage. Wood substance includes the chemical compounds making up the cell walls [cellulose, hemicelluloses and lignin] plus extractives and other substances such as starch and minerals present in the cells. With timber just cut from a tree this moisture percentage can regularly be in the 30% to 40% range for hardwoods and much higher in softwoods. Timber that is seasoned is usually defined as being between 10% and 15%. Timber that is seasoned is often referred to as KD [kiln dried] even though it may have been air dried.

Testing for moisture content

Several ways have evolved over time in defining moisture content. One was the weight of the water as a percentage of the total weight of the wood plus the water. The weight of the water was secured by oven drying a sample. So if the sample of wood plus the water was 100 grams and weight of the water was 30 grams the percentage water was 30%. This method always gave a percentage less than 100%. However the acknowledged method now is to use the following formula.

$$\% \text{ moisture content} = \frac{\text{initial weight} - \text{the oven dry weight} \times 100}{\text{oven dry weight}}$$

As an example consider a case where the initial weight was 100 grams and the oven dry weight was 80 grams. Using the formula above:

$$\% \text{ moisture content} = \frac{100 - 80}{80} \times 100 = \frac{20 \times 100}{80} = 25\%$$

Slight variations of this formula do exist but they end up giving the same result. However it must be kept in mind that in practice on site moisture contents are usually determined by a moisture meter. Thus the foregoing only applies when it is desired to use the results of an oven dry test and apply the formula quoted above for some particular reason.

Oven Dry Weight

In a few species that have a small content of volatile extractives such as turpentine these substances are also driven off in the oven drying so that the true moisture content can be slightly overstated with such species.

A Resistance Meter

Electrical Resistance Meter

With the electrical resistance meter two probes are driven into the timber and the electrical resistance between the probes measured. The principle used is that dry timber is basically a nonconductor but as the moisture content increases so the conductivity increases. A reading of moisture content can then be read off a calibrated scale. The instruments are calibrated against the results of the oven dry test using the species Douglas Fir [Oregon]. Different species have a small correction factor [up or down] to be applied to the reading. There is also a small correction to be applied if the temperature is above or below 20 degrees centigrade. These correction factors are supplied with the machine. The benefit of this instrument is the ability to take multiple moisture readings on site and get an immediate result instead of having to cut out a sample, send it way and then wait more than 24 hours for readings by the oven dry testing. As many tests as deemed necessary can also be taken in different parts of the structure to check for variations. As an example, if a timber floor is suspected having suffered water contamination, the area where this occurred can then be isolated. Tests can also be taken at different depths in the timber by driving the probes further in. As the moisture content of the top few millimeters of the surface of the timber can vary constantly with variations in daily humidity, to obtain a reading that is of any significance the probes have to driven at least 5mm to 6mm or more into the timber. However, to correctly assess the average moisture of a sample being tested on site, readings need to be taken at different depths and the readings averaged. Practically it is common to use the moisture reading at one third of the depth. For example, if a piece of 35mm thick timber is being checked the reading at about 12mm is taken as the average. The results obtained with this instrument, so long as it is checked regularly are usually within plus or minus one percent of the oven dry result. Normally this is sufficient to ascertain on site if there are moisture problems or check packs of timber to ensure they within relevant moisture specifications. This is a very useful reliable instrument with the only disadvantage being the necessity to leave holes in the surface. The photo below shows the probes that are driven into the timber and the section where the moisture content is read.

Pin type Resistance Meters

As well as the conventional resistance meters with hammer driven probes pin type meters are available. These work on the same principal as the resistance meter, are far more affordable but great care is necessary in interpreting the results because the pins only penetrate a few millimeters into the sample. They are useful for checking veneers, timbers of low thickness e.g., many internal mouldings. They are also helpful in getting an approximate moisture content when the timber being tested is obviously high in moisture content due to moisture contamination such as rain exposure or leaking plumbing.

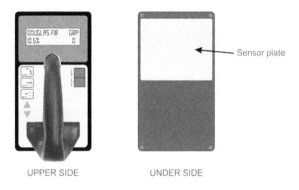

UPPER SIDE   UNDER SIDE

A Capacitance Meter

Electrical Capacitance Meter

Another instrument that is also used for testing the moisture content of timber is the capacitance meter. This meter measures the electrical capacity of the timber under the meter to hold an electrical charge. This varies according to the moisture content. The plate on the underside of the meter is placed on the surface of the timber and transmits the electrical impulse into the timber under the plate. These meters then measure this dielectric constant [capacitance] of the timber under where the reading is being taken with the instrument. This dielectric constant reading increases with increasing moisture content. It also varies according to the density of the timber. The reading given is the average moisture content under the plate. There is now a range of different instruments available which measure the moisture content down to different depths ranging from 8mm down to 25mm or more. The correct machine has to be selected according to the application. Using an instrument designed to measure to 25mm to measure the moisture content of 12mm thick flooring can give incorrect results as it could be giving the moisture content of underlying timber which could be entirely different. In using these machines, it is important to follow the instruments instructions. Some more sophisticated instruments allow correction for the density of the species being tested. However, this presumes the species being tested is identified and the density of this species is known.

Although not as accurate as a resistance meter they do provide a quick measurement and also do not damage the surface. The real advantage of this instrument is that it a large number of tests can be very quickly carried out. If desired, a 'correction' factor can initially be established by a preliminary test with a resistance meter to obtain a more accurate set of readings.

The instrument is also very useful if a large number of pieces of timber of varying moisture content in a pack of timber are to be checked with the added benefit of no holes that are left as with a resistance meter. A regular use is to quickly isolate high moisture content areas in a floor that has suffered water contamination from an unknown source. By carrying out a large number of tests on the total floor the source and extent of the contamination can then be established much more quickly than a resistance meter and also not damaging the floor with holes. A photo below relates to a capacitance meter. The sensing plate is the cross hatched area shown on the bottom view of the instrument.

Moisture in Timber and Fibre Saturation Point [FSP]

Fibre Saturation Point is a very important concept in the relationship between timber and moisture. To understand the concept, it is necessary to know of just where in the cell structure of timber the moisture situated. Moisture exists in both the cell cavities and the cell walls in green timber but in seasoned timber only in the cell walls. Sometimes the water in the cell cavities is referred to as 'free water.'

When timber is drying, moisture firstly comes away from the cell cavities and all this moisture has to be removed before moisture begins to come away from the cell walls. Once water begins to come away from the cell walls then the timber dimensions begin to change as the cells shrink in size. The moisture content at this point is called the fibre saturation point [FSP.] This means that a freshly sawn piece of timber will begin to lose moisture on exposure to the surroundings but its dimensions will not change until after the fibre saturation point [FSP] is reached. This is a very important concept. As previously discussed, the importance of having some knowledge of cell structure of timber makes an understanding of moisture much easier [see Chapter 4.] The moisture content of the timber at the fibre saturation point is variable and depends on the species and in turn the actual cell structure. Higher or lower fibre saturation points depend on the ratio of moisture in the cell cavities to moisture in the cell walls. Increasing moisture in the cell walls means higher fibre saturation points. Moisture contents of the timber at the fibre saturation point generally range from 20% to 30%.

There can also be a difference in the FSP between sapwood and truewood. If the truewood [heartwood] of timber contains a content of extractives in the cells there is therefore less water to come away. However, with the sapwood, because in the tree it has to freely transmit nutrients up and down the trunk and along the branches there is very little in the cell cavities. This then leads to a difference in the FSPs of species that are mostly sapwood such as pines to those with only a small sapwood band as with mature hardwoods. Obviously, species with a great proportion of sapwood have higher FSPs. Where the cell cavity is filled with extractives the percentage filled is also variable as happens with different species. This again leads to variation in the in FSP between different species. In the milling operation freshly sawn timber with higher FSPs will begin to shrink sooner than those with lower FSPs. It can therefore be seen that there are a number of variables affecting the percentage of moisture in timber at the FSP but the basic concept that timber does not begin to shrink until the fibre saturation point [FSP] is reached still applies. The opposite also applies when seasoned timber is subjected to large increase in moisture content as for example in an exposed deck. Expansion only occurs up to the fibre saturation point of the species i.e., the cell walls are filled with moisture. Moisture content can continue to increase but there is no further increase in size.

There is another situation that exists with larger section timber as the piece of timber is drying. As stated above no shrinkage occurs until the fibre saturation point is reached. However, the outer surface of a piece of timber can reach the fibre saturation point [FSP] and begin to shrink while in the inner sections no shrinkage occurs as the moisture content is still above the FSP. This situation is avoided in the commercial seasoning of lower thickness boards cut for use in flooring, decking and mouldings by the seasoning programmes that have been predetermined for the se. However, it does commonly occur in construction situations where large section unseasoned hardwoods are used for design and other reasons. Examples include large poles and unseasoned posts and beams. This can result in extreme stresses in the timber as the outer surfaces have shrunk and this is not matched by a corresponding shrinkage of the inner core. The result is checks and splits in the outer surfaces as they have to accommodate to the larger size of the underlying inner section of the timber. The situation can be alleviated somewhat by coating the outer surfaces with waterproofing solutions to slow the loss of water from the surface of the timber. The problem is not as[1]severe with softwoods because of lower shrinkage that occurs in shrinking from the unseasoned to the seasoned state. In the case of hardwoods once the whole piece of timber comes to the same moisture content it is not uncommon for the checks and splits to close up.

Timber Movement in Different Directions [Length, Tangential and Radial]

Understanding how much shrinkage or expansion in the various directions will occur as timber undergoes changes in moisture content is very important. There are three main factors to consider.

- The movement that takes place along the length, across the width and through the thickness of a piece of timber.
- The total shrinkage that takes place, up to and after the fibre saturation point has been passed to the point where the timber comes to equilibrium with the surrounding atmospheric moisture conditions.
- The movement that takes place either shrinkage or expansion with small changes in moisture content when timber is in the seasoned state.
- Dimension change in length, width and thickness with change in moisture content

This also involves whether the timber has been back sawn or quarter sawn. As explained in Chapter 2 on the conversion of the log into sawn timber, back sawn means the width of the piece of timber is tangential to the circumference of the log and the thickness is at right angles to the surface of the log [radial.] In quarter sawn timber the opposite occurs the width is at right angles to the surface of the log and the thickness is tangential. The whole point of knowing the method of sawing is that tangential movement is greater than radial movement and this lower movement radially is due to the constraining effect of the rays, the cells that run from the outside of the tree into the centre. This is illustrated on a cross section of a log showing where the back sawn member is cut and where the quarter sawn is cut. The sketch shows the width of the timber member not the depth.

As a rough approximation the tangential shrinkage or expansion is about twice that of the radial movement. It is normal practice to saw timber to the length of the log i.e., parallel to the long dimension of the cells. Lengthwise movement is therefore small as the lengths of the cells have minimal movement with the loss of water from the cell walls. In practice the increase in length can be ignored. As an approximation, the relationship length to radial to tangential is as follows

- Length Movement 1
- Radial Movement 50
- Tangential Movement 100

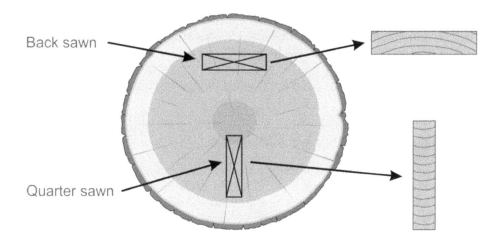

Back sawn

Quarter sawn

Back and Quarter Sawing

As an example, consider the approximate shrinkage of a piece of blackbutt that has been sawn tangentially [backsawn] with the dimensions 100mm wide 50 mm thick and 2.4 metres long and it is being dried to 12% moisture content. Blackbutt from various trees and areas can vary in shrinkage from green to dry but consider a typical example of tangential 8%, radial 4% and lengthwise 0.08%. When dried down to 12% moisture content the various dimension changes will be

- Width 100mm less 8% = 92mm [Loss 8mm in 100mm]
- Thickness 50mm less 4% = 48mm [Loss 2mm in 50mm]
- Length 2.4 metres less 0.08% = 2.398metres [Loss 2mm in 2400mm]

NOTE: It is important to understand that in normal practice in sawmills the length is rarely sawn exactly parallel to the edge of the log. However how much variation is allowed is covered by the grading standard on the allowable slope of grain. With timber sawn in a tangential direction there is also always some quarter sawn percentage and with quarter sawn there is a proportion of tangential sawn. Therefore, calculations as given above using the 1 to 50 to 100 ratio while giving a reasonable guide to the shrinkage that occurs in seasoning it is therefore not exactly accurate but does serve as an illustration.

In sawing unseasoned boards to 100mm for the production of flooring, decking etc., it is easy to see why after seasoning and then machining, quite a loss in size of from the original 100 mm occurs particularly with some hardwoods with higher shrinkage. For example - original width 100mm, after shrinkage in drying width 92mm, after machining 89mm

The above serves to show the relative loss of size as timber dries and the insignificant movement that takes place lengthwise. However, the calculations shown above can be worked and used on any species once its shrinkage characteristics are known and can then be useful in different building applications. In the appendix at the end of the book shrinkage data of a wide range of species is given.

The subject of movement that occurs once timber is seasoned and where different situations exist is covered in more detail in sections 7 and 8 of this chapter.

Shrinkage of Unseasoned Timber and its Implications

The amount of shrinkage that gradually takes place once the tree is felled, the log cut into sawn timber and the fibre saturation point is passed is very variable depending on the species and particularly on whether it is a hardwood or a softwood. Common tangential shrinkage of unseasoned pine down to the seasoned state [i.e., 12% moisture] is commonly 2.5% to 6% whereas hardwoods commonly vary from 6% to 13%. There are a few hardwood species that differ from these typical ranges. As an example, the imported hardwood species kwila and merbau have a tangential shrinkage from unseasoned to seasoned of around 2.5%.

For ease of reference, a table giving typical shrinkage data of more common species is included at the end of this chapter but as stated above a larger list of species is included in the Appendix section at the end of the book.

The implications of using unseasoned timber mean that the eventual loss in size of the timber member as it comes into equilibrium with the moisture conditions in the surrounding atmosphere has to be accommodated. Also, some degrade in the form of splits, checks and warping may affect the performance in the final use.

Examples of Using Unseasoned Timber and Applying Shrinkage Data

Knowing how much shrinkage will occur as unseasoned timber seasons naturally is very helpful when using unseasoned timber. Allowance can then be made for it in the construction process. Here are a couple of 'worked' examples to illustrate the point.

- A typical example is the use of larger section unseasoned hardwood as bearers and joists in domestic dwellings. If the plan calls for 150mm x 75mm bearers and 125mmx 50mm joists and the species used is blackbutt the eventual shrinkage can be calculated. Shrinkage tables show the shrinkage of blackbutt from the unseasoned state is 7.3% on average. The total depth of the bearers and joists will be 275mm [150mm +125mm] and shrinkage at 7.3% gives a total eventual reduction in depth of 30mm. If the total house is of timber construction the house will settle 30mm but if the house is brick or brick veneer which does not 'settle' serious problems arise and the use of seasoned timber, laminated

veneer lumber [LVL] for bearers and joists would be the preferred option.
- Another common example is the common use of unseasoned hardwood weatherboards as an exterior cladding. Obviously, the boards need sufficient lap to ensure adequate weather sealing once the boards have seasoned. With a 175 mm wide board and regular species used having round about 7% shrinkage when delivered to site, the boards will shrink by about 12mm. The regular procedure of using a 30mm lap then leaves a cover of 18mm when seasoned which is considered sufficient to prevent rain penetration. The common problem that occurs of exposure of the undercoat colour once the weatherboards have seasoned can be avoided by keeping the undercoat colour the same as the finish coat.

Many other examples exist and it is only a matter of applying the shrinkage data to ascertain the final timber dimensions once the unseasoned timber has seasoned to give the final situation for consideration.

Heart Shake in Timber

Heart in Timber

Firstly, the term heart in timber as used above should not be confused with the term used for hardwoods of heartwood [truewood], where the term is used to differentiate between heartwood and sapwood. As discussed previously in the tree transmission of fluids up and down the trunk only occurs in the sapwood as the cells in the heartwood are filled with other substances.

In the case of softwoods, heart is frequently found in sawn timber where it occurs under the major proportion of the wood which is sapwood. As the typical pine log is not large in diameter so the diameter of the heart is also small. As a result, as the heart comprises such a very small proportion of the piece of timber the relevant Australian Standard for Softwood 2858 for the visual grading, pith [heart] is unlimited in all grades. The occurrence is thus not considered a problem. However, where the timber is being used externally and requires preservative treatment, if there is a very small heart component this is difficult to preservative treat. Heart in pine can be commonly easily seen in larger section landscaping timbers.

This inner heart is derived from the early stages of the tree growth as a sapling when the timber was all sapwood. In the forest at times termites can find it a convenient home even though the tree as a whole is not attacked. However, the problem with heart in material is that it can be susceptible to excess checking and splitting as it seasons. Normal sawmilling procedures minimize cutting into unstable heart [if it is present] and the hardwood grading standard covers any possible incidence of heart material. However, when very much larger sizes are needed and if smaller log sizes are being processed, heart in material may have to be included. Unseasoned timber supplied from the timber mill does involve some subsequent splitting and checking as it naturally seasons after use. Therefore, if unstable heart is present the possibility exists that this splitting and checking may be more pronounced.

When the timber being milled is being recovered from used or reject power poles the chances of it containing heart in material is great when larger sizes are being sawn. In addition, as power poles take many years to completely season the chances of this heart in material containing splits and checks also being unseasoned is considerable. Of course, normal logs from the forest are also unseasoned.

Normal seasoning of large section unseasoned timber from the mill after use in construction then normally will involve some small amount of checking and splitting. However, if it contains heart in material more serious checking and splitting will occur. When used in construction situations and replacement is considered necessary this can cause difficulties and added cost. The same applies to timber recovered from power poles. Outside exposure to the sun accentuates the problem. In essence if it is possible to avoid the use of heart in timber it is to be desired. As a general practice when using large section timber in exterior situations surface treatment with moisture repellants which slow the rate of drying is a very desirable practice. The photo below shows splitting in 125mm X 125mm piece of heart in hardwood timber. The split was approximately 6mm wide.

An interesting example of where a major use of heart in timber occurred in a timber structure was in Barcaldine in central Queensland. The Tree of Knowledge is an interesting and innovative use of timber. The architect who designed the structure, Mr. Brian Hooper, won a major award for the project. Although it has little to do with the subject matter of this book the author felt readers might be interested in the brief history behind this quite unique timber structure.

Tree of Knowledge

In the mid 1800s a shearers' strike was held under the shade of a ghost gum tree [*e.papuana*] in Barcaldine to demand better pay and conditions. It is understood that this eventually led to the beginning of a political party. Ultimately the tree died, and it was decided to build a structure using the trunk, remaining branches and roots of the original tree, and this was enclosed in a timber structure with a clear plastic floor to show the roots. To simulate the canopy some 3600 pieces of 125mm x 125mm x 1.8metres long hardwood were suspended at varying heights from above. The sweep of the underside of the pieces, which are cut on on the lower ends at an angle, simulated the underside of the original tree canopy. This requires a little imagination but at night when lit with green lights it does give the desired idea. Public reaction to the whole structure varies from favourable to to very unfavourable. The timber used was cut from used reject power poles and, because of the size [125mm x 125mm], necessitated having to use heart in timber. Because the public can walk underneath, safety is very important. Initially regular inspections were required particularly at the point of suspension where, because it is heart in timber, it is subject to major splits, so it is vital to remove any faulty pieces that might cause them to drop.

Overall, the removal of fewer than one hundred of these [3%] affected by either the development of serious splits and checks near the point of support or compromise on the integrity of the member as a whole was required. With such a large number of pieces of heart in timber this would tend to indicate that, while heart in timber may be present, it might not always be a major problem. The photo taken by the author, shows the original trunk of the tree and some of the 3600 pieces of hardwood.

Unit Movement

Unit movement is a term used to define the percentage change in dimension, either shrinkage or expansion that takes place in the width or thickness of a piece of timber for a 1% change in moisture content for timbers that have been dried below the fibre saturation point. It is a very useful tool in calculating movement that will occur as the timber adjusts to the atmospheric moisture conditions. This may be small in internal situations or larger outdoors in situations such as decks.

Tables showing the average tangential figures for some common species are listed at the end of this chapter. However, these are quoted as 'average' as they can vary within a species. The term movement includes shrinkage as the timber dries further and expansion as it takes up moisture from the surrounding atmosphere. Most common Australian eucalypt hardwoods have a unit tangential shrinkage in the range of 0.3% to 0.4% while softwoods such as pine are around the 0.25%. Unit movement data in the tangential direction are different to those in the radial direction. In determining the movement in one direction it is therefore important to check whether the board or piece of timber has been tangentially [back] sawn or quarter sawn.

Calculating Timber Movement in Seasoned Timber Using Unit Movement

Knowing how to apply this unit movement data can be useful in many situations. For example, in the case of external decking the expansion gap required between boards can be calculated. If 90mm wide tangentially sawn spotted gum is taken, the gap between each board could be calculated as follows.

- Moisture content at time of laying 12%
- Moisture content at the FSP when rain wet 20%
- Increase in moisture content 8%
- Unit movement for species used 0.38%
- Board expansion = 90mm x 0.38% x 8 = 2.75mm

The standard recommendation of 3mm between boards covers this expansion. However, if 140mm decking boards are being laid, a wider gap is needed as follows:

- Board expansion = 140mm x 0.38% x 8 = 4.25mm

Therefore, a 5mm gap would be needed.

NOTE: It is difficult to apply the concept of using unit shrinkage to the laying of solid timber tongue and groove strip flooring to determine expansion gaps as there are many other factors in the total amount of expansion that can occur across the widths of timber floors. Qualified floor layers follow standard procedures for expansion gaps to be allowed for board expansion. The Australian Timber Flooring Association [ATFA] for example covers expansion in their recommendations which is not only based on theoretical data but years of practical experience.

Movement of Seasoned Timber

Once timber has been seasoned, it will no longer subject to the order of shrinkage that occurs when unseasoned timber dries down to the seasoned state. However, even when fully seasoned timber will undergo some movement as it expands and contracts with changes in the moisture content of the atmosphere to which it is exposed. This may be in fully protected internal situations where atmospheric moisture changes are not excessive such as timber strip flooring and decorative paneling. Alternatively, where seasoned timber is used externally as in decking, greater movement can be expected. The amount of movement that can be expected was calculated above for a couple of situations under the section on unit movement.

Timber Moisture Content and Atmospheric Moisture Content

As mentioned earlier timber is a hygroscopic material which means it will tend to assume the moisture content of its surroundings. An understanding of what is the relationship between the moisture content of a piece of timber and the moisture content of the surrounding atmosphere is very important.

Atmospheric Moisture Content – Definition of Relative Humidity

Atmospheric moisture content is reported as the relative humidity expressed as a percentage. This can be defined as the actual amount of moisture in the air compared to the situation where the air is fully saturated, i.e., the air will not hold any more moisture [at this point the relative humidity is 100%.] How much moisture the air will hold depends on the prevailing temperature, the higher the temperature the greater the amount of moisture the air can carry. To illustrate this, fully saturated air at 15 degrees C contains 12.7 grams of water per cubic metre. Raise the temperature to 25 degrees C and the moisture content when the air is fully saturated rises to 23 grams per cubic metre [an 80% increase] Raise it to 35 degrees C and the moisture in the air is 300% higher than air at 15 degrees C. Therefore, if the relative humidity is 60% at 15 degrees C then the air contains 7.6 grams of moisture per cubic metre [60% of 12.7] Both humidity and temperature affect the comfort of humans be it too high or too low. Higher temperatures in tropical regions means relative humidities can be higher in rainy conditions. Very low relative humidities can similarly cause human discomfort. Air conditioners, as well as lowering the temperature, make conditions better by lowering the humidity considerably. Of course, the term 'comfort' zone does not apply in the use of timber. However, an understanding of how to correctly use timber under different atmospheric moisture conditions is very important.

Equilibrium Moisture Content [EMC]

The Equilibrium Moisture Content of timber is the term which gives the moisture content of the timber when it has come into equilibrium with the surrounding atmospheric conditions. This is specific for a given time and varies during the day. To arrive at this moisture content, it is necessary to know the actual moisture content of the surrounding air. Calculation of this moisture content using basic data was explained above under the definition of relative humidity.

The determination of the Equilibrium Moisture Content has been simplified by calculation of the moisture content for a range of relative humidity and temperature conditions as either a chart or a list of numerical figures. By using either the EMC is easily and quickly determined. As the Bureau of Meteorology are already tracking climate data daily this then gives a ready reference to use for a large number of different locations around Australia. While EMCs can be used in covered external conditions the normal application is in internal applications. The term EMC is widely quoted but frequently not well understood.

As mentioned, the temperature and relative humidity vary during the day so does the EMC. However as far as the timber is concerned this change in moisture content is not instantaneous as it takes time for the timber to either take up moisture or release it. Obviously, also the larger the timber cross-section, the slower do changes occur. In most applications in the use of seasoned timber in internal situations it is vital that the designer and the person using the timber know firstly what is the moisture content of the timber about to be used and secondly what variations in the moisture content of the timber will occur through the range of atmospheric moisture conditions that apply over a twelve-month period for the site in question. By knowing these variations in moisture content of the timber, the amount of shrinkage or expansion can then be calculated and allowance made for it in the design. As explained previously timber is a hygroscopic material whose moisture content comes into equilibrium with the moisture in the surrounding atmosphere and its moisture content will follow changes in atmospheric moisture conditions. These conditions vary according to the geographic areas from high moisture in tropical monsoonal areas to low moisture conditions in dry arid inland areas. However, timber moisture conditions in subtropical and temperate areas closer to the ocean are not subject to such extremes. Some applications, for example the laying of solid timber strip flooring and internal paneling require that the user have this moisture information. Allowance then for movement [particularly expansion] as already mentioned above in the timber can then be made.

As mentioned above the source of the information required to calculate the EMC is the Commonwealth Bureau of Meteorology [BOM] who daily have available on line under the heading CLIMATE DATA the climate statistics for a very large number of locations around Australia. This climate data it is presented in the form of the monthly figures including the current day. This includes the temperature and relative humidity which are required for calculation of the EMC. This climate data includes the temperature and relative humidity readings for 9am and 3pm. It also includes other data for the day including for example rainfall, hours of sunshine and wind speeds. It is a very comprehensive document. As every individual temperature is not listed, it is allowable to interpolate between adjacent listed figures. As mentioned above with a knowledge of the variations in EMC derived from the Bureau of Meteorology information, movement in the timber for the job in question can be allowed for.

As an example, in using the above chart, take an example where the temperature is 25 degrees Celcius and the relative humidity is 65%.

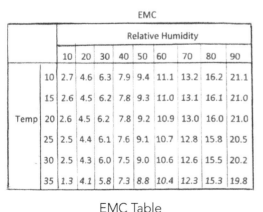

EMC

		Relative Humidity							
		10	20	30	40	50	60	70	80	90
	10	2.7	4.6	6.3	7.9	9.4	11.1	13.2	16.2	21.1
	15	2.6	4.5	6.2	7.8	9.3	11.0	13.1	16.1	21.0
Temp	20	2.6	4.5	6.2	7.8	9.2	10.9	13.0	16.0	21.0
	25	2.5	4.4	6.1	7.6	9.1	10.7	12.8	15.8	20.5
	30	2.5	4.3	6.0	7.5	9.0	10.6	12.6	15.5	20.2
	35	1.3	4.1	5.8	7.3	8.8	10.4	12.3	15.3	19.8

EMC Table

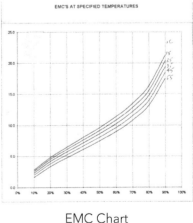

EMC'S AT SPECIFIED TEMPERATURES

EMC Chart

Putting these into the table or reading the chart the EMC can be read off as 11.7%. Or in other words when the timber is in equilibrium with the surroundings at the above temperature and relative humidity its moisture content will be 11.7%.

However, it is necessary in using these calculations to also check what is the EMC range over the year from conditions of high relative humidities and temperatures to lower relative humidities and temperatures. In deciding what should be the moisture content for the timber at time of installation, it is vital to know whether temperatures and relative humidities are at the high end or low end of the yearly movement. For example, if installation is occurring at the midpoint of the yearly range and this range in EMC is from 8% to 18% it would be desirable to use timber with a moisture content at the midpoint around 13% at the time of use. This of course also requires that the user know the moisture content of the timber being used or test for it with a moisture meter. The Australian Standard for kiln dried timber is 10% to 14% so packs of timber cannot be used without checking. This then may require that the moisture content of the timber will have to be adjusted [acclimatized] to the correct level. This particularly applies to areas where high or low EMCs are the norm. However, in areas where high EMCs can occur during the year it is not always possible to acclimatize and the recommended procedure e.g., for strip flooring is to allow extra expansion provisions. Care has also to be taken in the use of timber in continuously air-conditioned buildings where the EMCs are usually lower. In Chapter 11, there are some cases where the above information was not kept in mind. For example, one case study covers the problems which occurred in north Queensland which did not follow recommended procedures involving EMC.

A map which was produced a long time ago by the CSIRO shows the annual average typical EMC readings across Australia. It also illustrates that extensive areas in inland Australia fall into the very low EMC ranges. Unfortunately, no more recent edition has been produced. While the map on the next page does provide useful guidance regarding EMCs to be expected, to be precise it is necessary to obtain up to date EMCs for any specific area using current Bureau of Meteorology data and the procedures outlined above.

Shrinkage and Unit Movement of Some Common Species

The shrinkage of a few commonly used timbers in drying from the unseasoned state to 12% moisture content expressed as the percentage tangential shrinkage and the unit movement as a tangential percentage are listed below. It is important to note that these are average figures only due to the many variables that exist such as the area where the tree was grown and the age of the tree from which the timber was sawn that can affect the data. The data applies to the width of a board or in the case of heavier members such as joists and beams the depth. A more complete coverage of species for these data is given in the Appendix after Chapter 12.

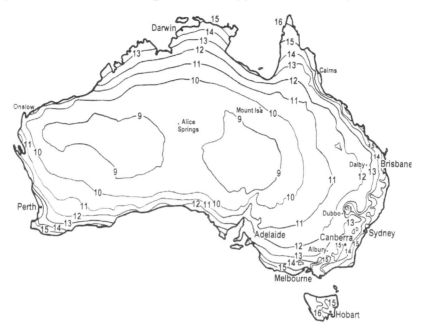

Map of Australia with EMC Levels

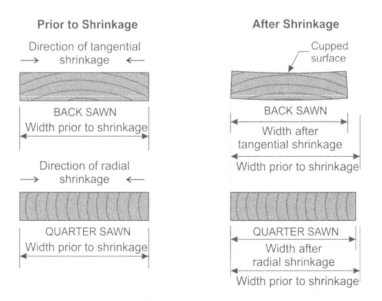

Shrinkage Rates

Species	Tangential Shrinkage %	Tangential Unit movement %
Blackbutt	7.3	0.37
White Cypress Pine	2.5	0.26
Grey Ironbark	7.5	0.39
Hoop Pine	3.8	0.23
Jarrah	7.4	0.30
Kwila	2.5	0.21
Meranti light red	5.0	N/A
Radiata Pine	5.1	0.27
Spotted Gum	6.1	0.38
Tasmanian Oak	13.3	0.36

Radial shrinkage is approximately half of the tangential shrinkage. Similarly, the unit radial movement is also much lower. Therefore, it is necessary to apply the right data when considering timber that has been quarter sawn. For example, in considering 100mm x 25mm quarter sawn boards the radial shrinkage applies to the 100mm dimension and the tangential shrinkage applies to the 25mm dimension. Alternatively, for a tangentially [back] sawn boards the opposite applies viz. the tangential shrinkage applies to the 100mm dimension and the radial shrinkage applies to the thickness [25mm].

Chapter 7: Degradation Of Timber

The term is used to cover the downgrade of timber that can occur in service due to a variety of causes. The chapter is divided into three sections.

- Durability and Decay
- Preservative Treatment of Timber
- Deterioration in Service by other factors and agents

Durability and Decay

This section covers decay due to fungal attack of timber.

Definition of Durability

The term durability is normally defined as the ability of timber to resist degradation when subject to attack by a wide range of different biological agencies particularly fungi.

For degradation by fungal attack conditions have to be suitable for it to occur. This is a basic requirement. Fungal attack of timber does not occur if it is in dry interior situations or in exterior situations where the moisture content is not consistently between 20% and 60%. Wood recovered from the tombs of the Pharaohs was found to be in very good condition because it was always dry and over the centuries these tombs had not been opened and not exposed the other factors listed in this chapter.

Decay Due to Fungal Attack

One of the most common factors that affects timber's durability is decay due to fungal attack. As it affects the strength and life of the timber it is a problem that has to be overcome. On the other hand, in the forest it is an important part of natural processes in returning fallen trees and branches plus other forest litter back into the soil.

For fungal attack to occur the following conditions need to exist.

- The moisture content in the timber must be suitable for fungi to grow, and this is normally between 20% and 60%.
- There must be an adequate supply of oxygen. Timber at considerable depths in the ocean does not decay because of lack of oxygen.
- The range of temperature must be suitable for the lifestyle of the different types of fungi. Decay in tropical regions is far greater than in Arctic regions.

- Suitable nutrients for the fungi to feed on must be present. Because of the chemical substances that can be present in the cell cavities, some species are extremely resistant to fungal attack i.e., the nutrients are not suitable.

It should be noted that the term 'dry rot' is frequently used to describe decay by fungi but, in reality, fungi need moisture to grow. The term is generally considered to come from the appearance of the residue left after fungal attack that has subsequently dried out.

Common Types of Fungi

Fungi are primitive forms of plant life that that have developed from spores under suitable conditions. They are different from other members of the plant kingdom in that they do not contain chlorophyll which is essential for photosynthesis to occur. They are also a different life form to bacteria which can also be found in timber. Unlike fungal attack bacterial degradation of timber is not as common but can occur very special situations such as in high moisture situations such as cooling towers. Fungal spores send out filaments called hyphae which break down the cell structures into their component chemicals on which the fungi feed. Apart from the types of fungi that attack timber, a wide range of other fungi exist in nature. Some of these are well known as for example those types of mushrooms [fungi] which have been found to be suitable for human consumption.

With regard to fungi attacking timber these are commonly classified as white rots, brown rots and soft rots.

White Rots

White rots break down both the cellulose and lignin that go to make up the cell wall of timber. The residue left is white in colour hence the name. The timber tends to break down along the length of the timber, not across it. Considerable damage can be caused depending on the severity of the fungal attack. This includes loss of strength and weight and very frequently has to be replaced.

Brown Rots

Brown rots only attack the celluloses in the cell wall leaving the darker coloured lignin. Hence the name brown rot. Unlike white rot, deep cracks occur both along the timber and across it which often gives it a cubical appearance on the surface. The surface also frequently exhibits an appearance as if it has been burnt. As with white rots the timber is badly damaged and has to be replaced.

Brown Rot

White Rot

Soft Rots

The third type of fungi attacking timber are the soft rots which are quite different from white and brown rots. Attack by these types of fungi result in cavities in and along the lengths of the cell walls. One result of this is the surface of the timber is very soft as it dries and can easily be scraped away. As with white and brown rots, the degradation of the timber causes a loss in strength and a loss in weight and frequently requires replacement.

In the photos above, one is of decay caused by white rot with the typical yellowy white appearance, the other is of brown rot and exhibits the typical appearance as described above under brown rot.

Sap Staining

Newly sawn unseasoned timber can be subject to sap staining which usually gives it a blue colour. Hoop and other pines are very susceptible particularly in the summer months. While this has very little effect on the strength of the timber it can seriously affect its appearance which in some applications is important. It particularly occurs in the time after the log has been felled and before the sawn timber has had a chance to dry out to below 20% moisture content. Passing the timber immediately after it has been sawn through a bath containing special anti-sap stain chemicals is very effective method of control. This is necessary where the sawn boards will be seasoned and machined into applications like flooring, paneling and internal joinery. While dressing the sawn boards can remove the staining, this at times is not possible as the stains are often very deep. Therefore, the use of anti-stain dips is very important.

Natural Durability Ratings

The natural durability of a species and in turn its ability to resist fungal attack is greatly conditional on the extractives that have been laid down in the cell cavities in the heartwood. These extractives give the heartwood the ability to resist fungal attack and the degree of resistance depends on the nature of the extractives. As a result, different species are rated differently on the durability scale. Durability ratings of some of the more common species are listed later in the chapter.

On the other hand, because the sapwood was still conducting plant nutrients up and down the tree when the tree was felled the cells are not filled with extractives that can impart some resistance to decay. Therefore, all sapwood is open to fungal attack and has no natural durability. For this reason, all sapwood is ranked in the lowest class of natural durability viz. class 4.

To simplify the use and correct application of the various species of timber in the many and varied applications, durability ratings have been established in regard to fungal attack. There are four classes 1 to 4 with Class 1 having the highest durability. These ratings are established by testing of individual species under conditions where fungi can exist. These ratings cover two categories where timber is in a moist environment. These are:

- Exterior out of ground contact
- In ground contact

This testing is carried out on the heartwood only because as mentioned above, the sapwood of all timbers is not durable to fungal attack. As a generalization many species of softwoods e.g., pines because they are predominantly composed of sapwood also have low natural resistance.

Above Ground Durability

As mentioned above there are four classes of natural durability and a few examples of species of timbers that meet each of the relevant classes for above ground durability are listed.

- Class 1: Hardwoods such as ironbark, tallowwood, forest red gum, bloodwoods, spotted gum, white mahogany, turpentine, kwila and teak plus cypress pine
- Class 2: A range of other hardwoods e.g jarrah, karri, Sydney blue gum, New England blackbutt, flooded [rose] gum and western red cedar
- Class 3: Other hardwoods such as messmate, alpine and mountain ash often grouped as Tasmanian Oak, brush box and silver ash
- Class 4: All sapwood, most pines and a number of soft hardwoods like meranti.

In Ground Durability

Because fungal attack is so much more severe, where the timber is in the ground or in contact with the ground and can be persistently moist many timbers that classed as 1,2 or3 in exterior out of ground situations have a lower rating in the in-ground situations.

Even though the durabilities of the different species are listed in the various classes, there is still some variability in durability within a species due to a number of factors such as the age of the tree when logged and the area where it was grown.

In-Ground Durability

In the same way as given above for examples of species meeting the four durability above ground classes, here is a similar listing for in-ground durabilities.

- Class 1: Eucalypt hardwoods such as tallowwood, ironbarks, bloodwoods, grey gum, white mahogany, forest red.
- Class 2: Other hardwoods such as spotted gum, jarrah, blackbutt, New England blackbutt turpentine.
- Class 3: Hardwoods including brush box, karri, messmate, Sydney blue gum, flooded [rose] gum.
- Class 4: Mountain and Alpine ash, soft hardwoods such as meranti and pines except a few like cypress, huon and celery top.

Note: all sapwood on hardwoods and pines is Class 4.

In the above lists, the common species names are given. However, the common names given for a given species can vary around different areas of Australia and the common name given in one area may be given to a different species in another area. The matter can be clarified by referring to information in the Appendix, which in addition to listing information on the more common species also includes the botanical names.

Life Expectancy

As a very rough rule of thumb the life expectancy of each class is as follows:

External exposed out of ground:

- Class 1: 40 years or more
- Class 2: 15-40 years
- Class 3: 7-15 years
- Class 4: 0-7 years

In-ground:

- Class 1: 25 years or more
- Class 2: 15-25 years

- Class 3: 5-15 years
- Class 4: 0-5 years [preservative treatment is required]

These are very rough guides due to the variability in the durability of the species within the class and the great variation in moisture conditions according to the site, average weather conditions and geographic location.

Unfortunately, there is a misconception among some users that because the timber is a hardwood it has high durability and therefore is suitable for all exterior above ground applications. This is not the case and reference to hardwoods in the examples of species in the different classes show eucalypt hardwoods in Class 3. These species are therefore not suitable for common external applications such as in decks and pergolas where a minimum durability of class 2 is recommended. Other timbers that are botanically classed as hardwoods such as meranti but are used for mouldings are Class 4 and not suitable for external exposed conditions.

If selecting or being offered a species for an exposed above ground or in ground application relying on the natural durability to prevent rot and decay, great care is necessary. It is wise to refer to the examples of timbers in the different durability classes above to check which species are suitable. A full listing of the natural durabilities of the more common species is also available in the Appendix. As a general rule a Class 2 or better durability timber is required for timbers being used in external exposed above ground situations and a Class 1 required for in ground situations. It is also important to remember that the timber has to be free of untreated sapwood as this has a Class 4 durability rating. If none of those species available meet the criteria, a selection will have to be made from a suitably treated timber [refer to the H1 to H6 listing] in the preservation section.

Preservative Treatment of Timber

As a very large percentage of Australia's timber resources and in particular the plantation pines have low durability the preservation of timber against degrade by fungi and insects by using different chemicals becomes an economic necessity. The basic principle is to fill the timber's cell cavities with preservative following the recommended procedures. In the case of hardwoods, while this treatment can be carried out on the sapwood, treatment of the truewood is generally not possible as the cell cavities are already full of extractives. In the great majority of applications this treatment of the sapwood of hardwoods is essential to prevent attack by fungi, termites and insects. Once the sapwood has been appropriately treated the durability of a particular species of hardwood against fungal and insect attack then comes back to the truewood's basic durability which in turn depends on what extractives are present in the cell cavities. As noted previously this varies from species to species.

Preservative treatment of sawn timber, round timber Glue laminated timber, LVL, plywood, etc are covered in the *Australian/New Zealand Standard AS/NZS 1604.1*. This is a very comprehensive standard covering the different levels of treatment for the different hazards, the different chemicals used and the penetration levels required. Also included are the branding requirements for timbers over specified minimum sizes. This branding includes the plant number, chemicals used and the level of treatment carried out. As an example, if the branding was 099 68 H3, the plant number was 099 (alternatively, the company name can be included), the treatment chemical mix as listed in the standard was 68 and the treatment level was H3. The standard allows the brand to be in a straight line or enclosed in a circle. If larger section timber is not branded then there is no guarantee that the timber has been treated in accordance with AS 1604.1. In the Standard it is not mandatory that smaller thicknesses and sizes be branded.

The standard also lists the recommended treatment levels for a wide range of timber products. For example,

- Bridges and Wharves H5
- Jetties H4
- Decks H3

Some Preservation History

Over a long time, different chemicals and other substances such as used automotive sump oil have traditionally been used to preserve timber against decay. One chemical that has been used for a long time is creosote which is derived from coal tar and still is still listed in the standard. However, this chemical is best kept for high hazard situations such as marine piles and associated timberwork and bridge timbers away from people contact. It is a skin irritant if used where people can touch it. Another chemical that has been used for a long time is borax and other compounds containing boron which are still listed to protect timber against attack by certain species of insects. It is incorporated in some of the current preservation blends. When used by itself in interior situations it is effective but in exterior situations the borax can be leached out by rain.

The metal copper for a long time has been a basic element in the control of fungi not only in timber but in other applications subject to the influence of fungi. The development many years ago of CCA [Copper Chrome Arsenic] marked a major step forward in that it combined the copper with arsenic to also combat termite and insect attack. CCA is a mixture of compounds of copper, chromium and arsenic in solution in water. The copper is the fungicide, the arsenic protects against insects and the chrome forms a complex between the other two chemicals and also the timber i.e., locks them all together and prevents the CCA from leaching out. The product is impregnated into the timber using vacuum pressure treatment in a pressure tank using strictly controlled procedures to ensure complete penetration of the sapwood in hardwoods and softwoods. As there is negligible heartwood in plantation pines complete penetration of these products occurs.

Preservation of timber has resulted in the more efficient use of

A Vacuum-Pressure Treatment Plant   A Double-Vacuum Treatment Plant

Australia's timber resources. There is no better example than power poles where more trees meeting the minimum diameters required become available because treatment of the outer sapwood band. This saves having to reduce the diameter by removing the non durable sapwood. The photos show timber being loaded into two different types of vacuum pressure treatment tanks.

Chemicals Commonly Being Used For Preservation

Currently the main chemicals being used are CCA, ACQ [an alkaline copper quaternary compound], the copper azoles [copper tebucoazole and copper propriconazole] and chemicals to protect against insects such as permethrin, bifenthrin and similar chemicals and also boron compounds. Copper is still the essential element to protect against decay. Research continues by the major manufacturers to develop new, better and safer chemicals to use.

Houses built on concrete slabs have been popular for many years. However, to protect against attack by termites it is necessary to either treat the ground under the slab or around the perimeter or both. For a long time, the use of chlorinated hydrocarbons such as chlordane and dieldrin used to be the common practice. Even though they had long-term residual properties the use of these chemicals for in ground use as a preservative against insects [termites] was phased out many years ago because of proven adverse effect on human health. The replacement chemicals used under slabs and around building perimeters do not have the same long life and this has led to the development of extra ways of protection including the treatment of the framing timbers against termite attack.

Research in Europe and America raised concerns as to the safety of CCA used in preserving timber used in a number of situations because of the arsenic and chromium content. Its general use is now prohibited in these areas except for high hazard situations. In Australia the Australian Pest and Veterinary Authority [APVMA] regulates the use of agricultural chemicals in Australia. Wood preservatives are deemed to be agricultural chemicals. In 2012 the APVMA restricted the use of CCA chemicals for high contact structures including garden furniture, picnic tables, exterior seating, children's play equipment, patio and domestic decking and handrails. CCA may be used for all other treated products and the APVMA also ruled that products already treated with CCA did not have to be removed from service. The APVMA restriction was implemented under the 'precautionary principle' as there was not enough data to require CCAs complete removal. The restrictions were implemented as a precaution.

The current mixtures, which have replaced CCA as non-arsenic and non-chromium alternatives, are water based and are mixtures of copper azoles, alkyl copper quaternary compounds and other chemicals. The preservation process still uses vacuum pressure impregnation [like CCA] and manufacturers claim it provides good fungal protection to H3 and H4 levels plus protection against termites and borers as did CCA so long as recommended procedures are followed.

Another development has been the micronising [grinding to very small particles] of the required chemicals, then dispersing in water and finally pressure treating to fill the cell cavities. Micronised wood preservatives are an alternative to water soluble systems and can be used wherever water soluble preservatives are used. Pigments for tinting the timbers can also be part of the preservative mix.

LOSP [Light Oil Solvent Preservatives]

Vacuum pressure treatment using chemicals dissolved in water, while very effective, does require the timber to be redried after treatment. In so doing timber degrade in the form of twisting and warping can occur. This has led to replacing the water with a light petroleum solvent and using chemicals that will dissolve in the solvent. This is carried out in a similar pressure tank using vacuum and pressure to achieve full penetration. The procedure recommended requires that the timber is removed from the pressure vessel and allowed to drip dry and the treatment chemicals can then be recovered back into the treatment vessel. The reason for this procedure is to ensure the timber is free from solvent containing the preservative on the surface. The chemicals used vary according to the type of hazard shown in the H1 to H6 table below. The minimum levels of retention of the various chemicals in the different hazard classes are specified in the *AS/NZS 1604.1*. The standard also allows an envelope treatment where complete penetration is not carried out. Minimum depths of penetration are specified for various situations. In all applications where envelope treatment has been carried out the manufacturers of the chemicals recommend that all sawcuts, drilling, notching and any surface machining or heavy sanding, the timber areas affected be subsequently treated with a remedial preservative such as copper or zinc naphthenate if the product warranty is to be maintained.

Copper naphthenate dissolved in petroleum solvent can also be used to surface treat timber by painting on in other situations where extra treatment is required. The product is made by combining copper with naphthenic acid sourced from some types of naphthenic based crude oil [particularly Middle Eastern crudes.] The copper gives protection against fungi and the naphthenate protection from insects such as termites and borers. However it should be noted that brushing or spraying timber preservative does not penetrate very far into the timber and must be applied regularly [e.g., annually] if long term protection is required.

As set out in the standard AS1604.1 there is a set of Hazard Classes for timber that has been preservative treated that covers the different levels of biological hazard. This, of course, is in addition to the natural durability ratings [1 to 4] covering the hazard conditions of the truewood or heartwood of all species to which the timber is exposed as explained previously.

The ratings are H1 to H6 with H6 being the highest rating:

Hazard Class	Exposure/Service Condition	Biological Hazard	Typical Uses
H1	Interior situations only	Lyctid type borers	panelling, flooring where susceptible timber used
H2	Interior situations only	Borers and termites	Framing, flooring etc. for species with no natural resistance
H3	Outside, weather-exposed, moderate decay plus	Out-of-ground borers and termites	outside construction, incl. decks, pergolas, weatherboards
H4	Outside in-ground situations, severe decay	termites	posts, landscaping

H5	Outside in-ground with very severe decay conditions	Very severe decay, plus termites and borers	Poles and timber in fresh water, piles, major retaining walls
H6	Sea water exposure,	decay and marine creature attack	wharves, boat hulls jetties

NOTES: [i] As is obvious the higher the H rating the higher the concentrations of preservative; [ii] In the treatment of the sapwood of hardwoods to the different levels, for the selected timber to be suitable the basic durability of the truewood must also be suitable for the listed application.

Deterioration In Service – Other Factors And Agents

This section includes the following

- Insect attack by borers [beetles] and wood moths
- Attack by termites
- Attack by marine organisms
- Weathering
- Fire

Insect Attack [Borers and Wood Moths]

Throughout the world there are a vast number of different species of insects that attack timber or in effect make it their home. Many of these are specific to different geographic areas. In many countries insects also supplement the supplies of food for the population. In Australia there are also many species of insects which are widely distributed geographically around the continent where differing climatic conditions favour different species of insects. Many of the overseas species if they gained entry to Australia could seriously affect Australia's forests and timber industry and Australia's quarantine laws are in place to protect against their entry.

While such attack by insects is very real, it is most important to realize that, from the timber users' point of view and with the exception of insects which attack seasoned timber, this damage is caused before the timber gets into the user's hands. The effect of insect attack on timber can range from minimal damage to complete destruction. Holes in the timber can range in size from less than a millimeter to 25mm or more. The Australian grading rules set limits on the size and frequency of occurrence of holes according to the various products and grades. Obviously, appearance grade products like flooring, paneling and joinery where appearance is important have different grading rules to structural products where strength is the main criteria.

Borers that attack timber are commonly divided into two main groups

- Those that attack unseasoned [green] timber either in the tree itself and particularly in freshly felled logs and freshly sawn timber.
- Those that attack seasoned timber.

In both situations the damage can range from slight to extreme. Borers and wood moths that attack very young saplings can frequently cause the tree to die. Severe attack of some types of seasoned pine species can, after continued reinfestation, cause complete destruction of the timber.

Before considering the more common types of borers in each of the two categories above it is helpful to understand the life cycle of borers. In this way an understanding of what is going on inside the piece of timber is obtained and how damage is caused. There are four steps in a beetle's life cycle. It is interesting that some refer to these insects as borers and others as beetles, a borer when it creating holes, a beetle when it emerges and flies away.

- Initially the female adult insect lays eggs in cracks, crevices or pores in the timber or with some species bores into the timber so as to allow easy access for the next stage to get into the sapwood and truewood.
- Stage two involves the hatching of the eggs into larvae or grubs. These grubs then tunnel around inside the timber and feed on the wood substance. This is when the major damage is done.
- When fully grown the grubs turn into pupae and grow through a 'resting' stage prior to the formation of the adult insect.
- After hardening the pupae are transformed into the adult insect [the beetle] which bores its way out of the timber and flies away to find a mate. Then the whole cycle is again repeated. The time for whole process to occur is very variable and can be a matter of weeks up to many years.

NOTE: Unlike termites, in the case of beetles, it is the larvae [grub] stage that causes the damage to timber. The holes that appear on the surface of the log are mostly caused by the new beetles emerging but considerable damage inside the wood could have already occurred. When the log is being milled it is then that any damage done in the grub stage becomes apparent.

In Australia generally entomologists are knowledgeable about the more common insects [beetles] that exist and if required can be called upon to identify particular species. However, this is more often than not made more difficult by the fact that frequently the holes that appear are caused by the emergence of the beetle which is then not around to study. However, the shape, size and nature of the hole can frequently help. It is however unreasonable to expect Australian entomologists to be able to identify the myriads of species of insects that exist around the world but they do have specialized information on those species that pose a threat to Australia and where strict quarantine requirements have to be met.

Beetles Attacking Unseasoned [Green] Timber

Among the wide range of borers attacking green timber are Longicorn beetles, Auger beetles, Ambrosia beetles and Jewel beetles. Some species of these will also continue to attack the timber once it is becomes seasoned if the timber was air-dried. If the timber was kiln dried the heat is sufficient to kill the larvae remaining in the timber. One beetle that continues to attack seasoned timber is the hoop pine jewel beetle so long as the timber was air dried. A few brief notes on some of the list of beetles attacking unseasoned timber follows.

Longicorn Beetles [family Cerambycidae]

There are many varieties of this beetle and some attack only the sapwood of hardwoods, others only softwoods. Normally they require a plentiful supply of moisture in the timber so that once the timber begins to dry out fresh attack on fallen logs only rarely occurs. Holes can range in size up to 12mm and are usually oval in shape. In trees particularly eucalypts the holes and tunnels made, become filled with gum and become the source of gum veins and pockets. The sizes of different beetles vary according to the species but can be up to about 30mm long.

Auger Beetles [family Bostrychidae]

Many different varieties exist and vary from small to medium in size. The beetle bores a little way into the timber to lay her eggs. The holes made by the grubs are smaller than those from longicorns, being from 3mm to 6mm in diameter and are circular in shape. They are characterized by coarse frass in the exit holes. Auger beetles are widely distributed and generally are only found in the sapwood where they feed on the starch. They can be up to 20mm in length.

Ambrosia Beetles [Pinhole and Shot Hole]

The names given to these beetles are due to the nature of the holes they make and different varieties can belong to two different families [Platypodid and Scolytid]. They can seriously damage freshly felled logs both hardwoods and softwoods. Holes are small but damage can be severe due to the attack by myriads of these insects. One of the problems that can occur is that instead of the holes being scattered, holes can be found in a straight line [shothole] which can then seriously affect the strength of a timber member particularly if it across the length of the piece of timber.

Jewel Beetles [family Buprestidae]

So-called because of the iridescent appearance of the beetle which is 15mm to 20mm long. There are a large number of species that can attack numbers of different softwood species. They can cause severe damage to logs and sawn timber of species such as cypress. The life cycle can be many years in extent [unless the timber was kiln dried during the production process] and the insect can emerge many years after the timber has been used in construction. The holes are usually oval in shape.

The photographs shown do not indicate the size of the beetles but this is covered in the details on each beetle above. Three common beetles – Gum Tree Longicorn, Auger Beetle and Cypress Jewel Beetle – are shown below.

(left to right) Gum Tree Longicorn Beetle, Auger Beetle, Cyprus Jewel Beetle

Beetles Attacking Seasoned Timber

While a little knowledge of borers that attack unseasoned [green] timber is interesting, as pointed out earlier, this happens before the timber reaches the user and when the timber is being milled the standards control the sizes and numbers of holes allowed in each of the various grades. Beetles that attack seasoned timber that is already in use present an entirely different problem. The following types are important – Lyctus beetle, Furniture beetle, the Queensland pine beetle, European furniture beetle and the European house borer. Very brief notes on each follow.

Lyctus [Powder Post] beetles

Lyctus beetles, which are 3mm to 4mm long in the adult stage, attack the sapwood of both unseasoned and seasoned hardwood and can cause severe damage. In attacking seasoned timber considerable damage can occur after construction is complete to the extent that the whole sapwood band can be removed. With regard to hardwoods lyctus only target the sapwood of susceptible species where starch is usually present and where the pore size is large enough for the insect to deposit eggs in. This pore size criteria rules out many hardwood species [e.g., blackbutt] from attack by lyctus where the pore size is too small. This explains why the sapwood of some hardwoods is susceptible and why some are not. It also rules out non pored timbers such as pines. As the newly hatched insect emerges it leaves holes approximately 1.5mm in diameter and the powder like dust falling out of them is a good indicator of attack by this insect. The problem not only occurs with construction timbers but also hardwoods used in furniture manufacture.

Preservative treatment of the sapwood band prevents attack and, if this has not occurred, sealing all the surfaces of timber liable to be attacked with a good hard surface finish usually prevents the female from laying eggs.

Furniture Beetle [Anobium Species]

This beetle which is about 3mm long in the adult stage attacks the sapwood of pine and favours timber from seven years in age or over [by this time thoroughly seasoned] The beetle is usually brought into the dwelling from timber furniture that is already under attack. In this it is unlike lyctus where the beetle flies in from the outside surroundings. The insect can cause considerable damage to any pine particularly construction timbers, flooring, paneling furniture, etc. The best remedial action is usually to remove or treat the timber that was the original source of the beetle and replace any timber that has been attacked.

Queensland Pine Beetle [Calymaderus Incisus]

This is a very destructive beetle about 3mm long that is only found in S.E. Queensland where under favourable conditions it will attack hoop and kauri pines. It is frequently called the calamity beetle because of the damage it can cause. Unless preventative measures are taken it will re-infest until most of the timber is destroyed and the timber has no strength. Pine flooring is one use that that can be attacked from beneath. Preservative treatment of the timber before use is effective.

European Furniture Beetle

This is a very close relative of the Queensland pine beetle and is found in many parts of Australia. It attacks hoop pine and also softer hardwoods

European House Borer

This is a very destructive borer that came into Australia many years ago in imported furniture and prefabricated buildings. It still does occur in some areas but treatment of timber that has been attacked and quarantine measures have minimised its spread and damage in Australia.

Other Insects Attacking Timber

Wood Moths [family Cossidae]

Wood moths only attack living trees especially young ones, not sawn timber. The life cycle is similar to beetles and it is the grubs which cause the damage in a similar way to beetles. The adult moths lay eggs in the bark and the grubs burrow into the tree.

Moths vary in size from large to small and the Australian giant wood moth is one of the largest of the moth species in the world. It creates tunnels up to 25mm in diameter. As the moths only attack living trees, the damage is discovered once the logs are milled into timber. The size and numbers of holes, as with beetles, are covered by the relevant grading rules.

Two beetles are illustrated below, viz. [1] the Lyctus Beetle and [2] the Anobium Furniture Beetle [*anobium punctatum*]. Normal length of both beetles is about 3mm.

Lyctus (left) and Anobium (right) Beetles

Preventative Methods

In general, no methods are in place to stop insect attack of trees in the forest or freshly felled trunks or green sawn timber. However, some action has been taken to prevent dieback of eucalypts in some areas from specific insect pests. As regards seasoned timber used in construction damage can be prevented by preservative treatment. It is normal for producers of timbers where the sapwood is liable to attack by the lyctus borer [e.g., spotted gum] to treat the sapwood with an approved preservative before sale. With the other types of borers attacking seasoned timber such as some types of pine, as mentioned above, prior preservative treatment or shielding the timber with surface finishes from exposure to the flying insect can be used. The preservative treatment level H1 covers prevention against insect attack. With the wide range of insects, protection has to be tailored to the insect and the area and advice sought from the appropriate authority usually the Government Forestry Authority. Information on termites and beetles and photos courtesy of QLD Forestry brochures.

Attack by Termites

Termites are prehistoric insects and evidence of their existence dates back 50 million years. They can cause extreme damage to timber buildings. However, when found in the forest, like the fungi, they are an essential part of the ecosystem in that they return fallen or damaged trees and branches on the forest floor back into the ground. There is an extremely large number of termite species occurring around the world, but fewer than twenty are considered significant in attacking timber and timber-based products in Australia. The relevant standard covering termites and their management is Australian Standard 3660.1. This is an extremely comprehensive document. The subject is also covered extensively in the Building Code of Australia particularly from the aspect of protection of buildings from attack.

The main species attacking buildings and other timber can be grouped into two categories.

- Subterranian Termites
- Drywood Termites

Both need moisture to exist but the former get moisture from the ground while the latter obtain it from the timber they are attacking.

Termites are a social insect and the different members live together in colonies. In the case of subterranean termites, the colony consists of a king and queen, workers and soldiers, infantile termites and alates. They usually live below the ground typically in decaying stumps of former trees.

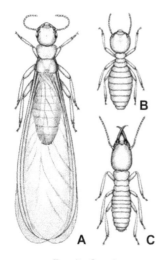

Termite Species
A = Alate
B = Worker
C = Soldier

The queen is the most important member as she can lay up to 2000 eggs per week and can live for 50 years. The eggs hatch to form the nymphs [infants] which then grow to become the other members of the colony. The role of the workers is to bring food [wood substance] to the colony by searching for and then attacking susceptible timber wherever it can be found. The role of the soldiers is to protect the colony from dangers [particularly ants]. At certain times of the year the winged alates are born and these fly off in summer in great numbers to become future queens and kings and start further colonies.

By subterranean termites is meant that the nest as mentioned above is usually underground from which the workers travel in underground galleries that are built to search for sources of food [timber] These galleries, which can extend up to 50 metres or more from the nest, ensure that the termites wholly move in a moist environment as drying out can lead to death of the termite. The galleries are commonly no more than 300mm below the surface of the ground. Both the workers and soldiers are blind, sterile and wingless. If these galleries which are approximately 6mm in cross-section are discovered around the perimeter of a structure it is a quick visual means of detecting the presence of termite activity.

The main species of subterranean termites attacking timbers in Australia are

- Four varieties of *coptotermes*
- Four varieties of *heterotermes*
- Four varieties of *schedorhinotermes*
- Three varieties of *nasutitermes*

In addition, there is the species *Mastotermes darwiniensis*, a large voracious mound-building termite found in northern Australia. These mounds are a familiar scene in many areas. The drawings show the different forms of the *coptotermes* termite, viz. A: the winged alate, B: the worker, and C the soldier.

Protection from Subterranean Termites

Because termites can cause so much damage particularly to domestic dwellings a great amount of effort has been made to develop procedures to prevent ingress of termites. Termites are widely distributed in areas north of the Tropic of Capricorn and the risk of damage is great. South of the Tropic covering the rest of Queensland and Western Australia and northern NSW, termite damage is still high but less than above the Tropic. Termite damage reduces with movement south so that risk is low in Victoria and considered negligible in Tasmania. In States such as Queensland where termites are more of a problem there are extra regulations. Both the *Australian Standard 3660.1* and the *Building Code of Australia* comprehensively cover the subject of termites and various methods of protection. It is wise for those involved in designing and building to get access to these documents plus any local regulations to use as references.

Protection against termite attack has also required more effort over the last 20 years in areas where termites are active because of a number of changes to building procedures. As mentioned previously one of the major changes was the banning of the use of organochlorine chemicals such as chlordane and dieldrin as termiticides for ground treatment. This step was wisely taken because they were found to be dangerous to human health and the environment in general. However, the organochlorines were very effective with a long in-ground life. The newer chemicals are safer but not as persistent in the ground and now annual inspections are considered a necessity. Other factors such as the change over from hardwood house framing much of which was resistant to termite attack to softwood framing and the increasing popularity of building on slabs have also had an effect.

The *Australian Standard 3660.1* and the *NCC BCA* give very comprehensive details with drawings of the various methods of protection both for slab on ground and high set housing. Included are details of various methods used including stainless steel mesh, the requirements if using chemicals both around the perimeter and under the slab and the use of termite resistant crushed aggregates. There are also recommendations and drawings on desirable slab design particularly slab edge design. The subject of protecting entry via drainage plumbing and piping is also covered. A copy of the Standards can be obtained from Standards Australia, 16 Bridge Street, Sydney, New South Wales. The standard is classed as a deemed to comply document under the rules of the *NCC BCA*.

Much is said on the use of termite resistant framing such as steel but if termites gain access, internal cupboards and joinery, flooring, skirting and architraves can be destroyed. The use of timber framing treated to be termite resistant is now widespread but the same comment as above still applies. This treatment however is beneficial as it does prevent damage to the building's basic structure. Also available is pine framing that has been treated to prevent decay of the structure. In treating against decay, the treatment also confers resistance to attack by termites.

In principle, protection against termites very much involves preventing termites gaining access to the structure through very many possible points of entry. Protecting timber against termites is an ongoing process so that extra attention has to be paid to driveways, decks and pergolas attached to the main structure and landscaping against the building. These works are frequently carried out after the building was completed so it is important that they do not compromise the original protection measures.

The Termite Resistance of Different Species

Some timbers have a natural inbuilt resistance to attack by termites. This is primarily due to substances present in the cells of the truewood. As an example, some species have silica present which grinds down their chewing mechanism and so termites avoid these species. Resistance is also conferred by other types of chemicals in the cells which adversely react with digestive systems of termites and again termites learn to avoid these species. However, where resistance is due to chemicals in the cells of the truewood the sapwood of these species is not immune to attack. Termites do not attack living trees except the inner heart or pith from which the tree began as a sapling which tends to no longer be solid timber. Trees can then be found with an inner heart full of termites. However, once the log is sawn the grading rules in place for the milled timber cover incidence of damage from termite attack and of course once removed from contact with the nest any living termites in the log being milled will die. If by error timber with termites still alive finds its way to a building site there is no danger of a nest being established as this requires the queen.

Preservative treatment of softwoods and the sapwood of hardwoods is essential in situations like landscaping and fencing where the timber is open to attack. If using hardwoods, the use of termite resistant species free of sapwood is considered necessary.

Note: The resistance of species to termite attack is extremely variable and there are many factors that cause this variability. Some factors that can affect the resistance include:

- Whether the exposure is in the ground or above ground [i.e., frequently moist or only intermittently wet]
- The termite species present
- With eucalypts whether the timber is from old growth or rapid growth [plantation] forests.
- Ground moisture levels.

Australian Standard 3660.1 lists a number of species with resistance to termites found south of the Tropic of Capricorn. The more commonly available of these are listed below. The special Tasmanian softwoods have been included for interest even though availability is limited and as mentioned termite risk in Tasmania is considered negligible. Many in the list are not resistant to Mastotermes, the voracious termite found north of the tropic of Capricorn.

Non-Eucalypts

Brush Box

Satinay

Turpentine

Eucalypts

Blackbut

New England Blackbutt

Coast Grey Box

Forest Red Gum

Gympie Messmate

Ironbark [Reds and Grey]

Jarrah

Red Bloodwood

Red Mahogany;

River Red Gum

Spotted Gum

Southern Mahogany

Stringbarks [White, Red and Yellow]

Tallowwood

White Mahogany

Australian Softwoods

Cypress [Black and White]

Huon Pine [Tasmania]

King William Pine [Tasmania]

Imported Softwoods

Redwood [America]

Western Red Cedar [America]

Imported Hardwoods

Burmese Teak

Kwila

Merbau

New Guinea Rosewood

NOTE: The resistance applies to the truewood only and is due to the substances in the cells. Any sapwood present has to be appropriately treated.

As pointed out above termite resistance can of course be given to non-resistant timbers such as the pines by appropriate preservative treatment to the recommended level. If the timber is also to be used in moisture exposed conditions either in ground or above ground the appropriate preservative treatment necessary to protect against decay also gives very adequate termite treatment.

Drywood Termites

While the main termite damage to timber in Australia is overwhelmingly due subterranean termites, drywood termites can cause damage usually to internal furniture and fittings. This species of termites has similar social colonies to the subterranean species. However, instead of building a nest underground male and female pairs commonly fly into dead trees, stumps or structures and then build a nest and develop a colony. Alternatively, they can be introduced into buildings and domestic houses in furniture or fixtures where they are already established. Like the subterranean termites they need moisture to exist but they take this from the timber they are attacking. The main native drywood termite in Australia is *cryptotermes primus*, and the main one that can come from overseas is *cryptotermes brevis*. The overseas termite is commonly known as the West Indian Drywood termite. Both can cause damage to houses, furniture and fittings but the overseas termite *c.brevis* is far more destructive. Australian Quarantine Authorities are extremely vigilant to prevent the entry of this termite. If any evidence is found of the entry of this termite into Australia either in timber or buildings, extreme measures are taken by Quarantine Authorities to destroy the termites by treatment with methyl bromide gas. As far as the native drywood termite, methods used in protection and elimination are different to those used with subterranean species. Where the introduction of infested furniture or fixtures is inadvertently been the cause of the introduction of *e.primus* the presence of piles of pellets [frass] around the furniture is a sure sign that the termite is present. Spraying the nest with an approved termiticide to kill the termites is an effective way of overcoming the problem.

Attack by Marine Organisms in Marine Environments

This is a very specialized application as it covers timber, primarily piles, used in the construction of wharves and jetties. Wooden boats can also be attacked if they are continually in situations where attack can occur e.g., always moored.

There are two main types of organisms:

- Molluscs [shells]
- Crustaceans.

The attack occurs in the open sea but this can extend some way up rivers and inlets throughout the world. Some species only exist in water with high salt content as in oceans, others in lower salt environments away from the sea. Attack can occur from the low tide level usually down to the sea floor but some only live higher up the timber structure between the low and high tide levels.

Molluscs

This type of organism covers the wide range of sea shells which may have one or two shells [valves] that occur around the world but the type that mainly attack timber are bivalves [two hinged shells] to which is

Shipworms, photo credit, Dr Laurie Cookson

attached a tail. The shells are designed to grind into the timber to secure the ground up wood as feed while the tails remains on the surface and siphons water and nutrients in from the sea water. Two well-known species are *teredo* which lives in water of high salinity and *nausitoria* which lives in low salinity water. Both can cause excessive damage even to timbers claimed to be resistant.

Crustacea

This species of organism is also widely distributed around the world. The crustacean genera also includes other well-known edible species such as crabs, crayfish and prawns. There are a number of types that attack timber and well-known examples are gribble and pill bugs, Holes are small from less than one mm up to 6 mm in diameter. Damage however can be severe due to great numbers of the species that can be present. Gribble and pill bugs are found only in high salinity water [3% or more] and thus tend not to be in tidal estuaries subject to flow from fresh water streams.

Timbers vary greatly in their resistance to marine borers. Those containing silica such as turpentine, satinay and brush box are highly resistant as also is the true wood of cypress pine which contains an extractive poisonous to molluscs and crustacea.

Protection

Many methods exist. In the case of boats, the best is to keep the boats out of water when not in use. Regular scraping down and coating with anti-fouling paints is commonly used to limit damage. As far as piles are concerned encasing them from the mud line and above with concrete pipes or similar is an effective method widely used. If it is possible to achieve proper penetration, preservative treatment to H6 level is an alternative. Creosote can also be used. Lastly resistant timbers such as turpentine can be used. Overall, many different methods are used.

Concrete encased pile with sand

Climate and Weathering

When fully exposed to weather conditions deterioration of timber will take place unless the timber has been fully protected by a surface film such as paint or other surface finishes. There are two types of deterioration that can occur:

- By solar radiation [UV]
- By alternate wetting and drying due to rain, dew and fog.

Solar radiation can cause chemical reaction within the surface layers of the timber and over time lead to break down of the timber. It can easily be seen by the 'greying' of the surface caused by the chemical decomposition of the organic pigments in the timber that gave it the original colour.

The rate of deterioration is dependent on

- the hours of sunshine
- the intensity of the solar radiation
- the time of the year.
- the orientation – north, south, east or west.

The intensity of radiation is dependent on the latitude, being much higher nearer the equator. However, because tropical areas are generally subject to greater rainfall and cloud cover the overall effect is to offset the higher intensity. The areas where greatest deterioration from solar radiation occurs are arid, desert areas closer to the equator. As an example, exposed timber in Alice Springs suffers much more than Melbourne in being closer to the equator and having far more cloud free days. The time of the year also affects the intensity of radiation being less in winter than summer and there are also less hours of sunshine in winter. Lastly the orientation is important. In the southern hemisphere for example where timber weatherboards are used as the external cladding, exposure to solar radiation is greater on the northern walls than those on the southern walls.

In summary it can be seen that there are a great number of factors affecting the chemical deterioration of fully exposed timber surfaces caused by solar radiation.

Protection Against Solar Radiation

Protection is best achieved by the use of protective films rather than letting the timber weather 'naturally'. The comments above also affect the life and efficiency of protective films. Those developed for use in milder, gentler climates such as Europe, Canada etc., may not necessarily give satisfactory service in many areas of Australia where solar deterioration is high. Lighter colour finishes reflect more of the radiation than dark colours. For example, a white painted surface reflects 50% more of the radiation than a black or a very dark coloured finish.

Climatic Effects Causing Alternate Wetting and Drying

The alternate expansion of the timber surface due to wetting from rain, heavy dew or fog and then the shrinking as the timber dries out under sunshine gradually leads to surface breakdown. Splits and checks develop which become worse over time and loss of surface layers of timber very slowly occurs. As with solar radiation this can be largely prevented by the use of good protective films. However, a recent refurbishment of a one-hundred-year-old building in southern Queensland was a good example of the gradual loss of surface layers of timber. The hardwood weatherboards had on the 25mm thicker side come down to 15mm. The boards had for a long time not been painted or protected.

Decks and Boardwalks

Because many decks are fully exposed to solar radiation and the weather, protection of the timber requires special consideration. Even though more costly than treated pine the use of durable selected species of hardwood such as spotted gum for the decking timber is a sound option. Where the deck is not large the regular application of good quality decking finishes proven under Australian conditions will give the necessary protection to the timber.

Fully exposed very large decks and boardwalks constitute a different situation. The cost of the regular application of decking finishes normally is prohibitive. Usually much thicker sawn finish decking timber is used as opposed to the dressed 19mm timber used in domestic applications. Regular inspection and replacement of badly deteriorated boards is the usual option. The use of very good quality decking timber in the original construction even though a little more expensive will save the costs of replacing decking that is no longer considered sound. To show how large some decks can be, a photo on the next page shows a very large deck on the Plains of Abraham in Quebec, Canada. Because of its size it has to weather naturally but fortunately the climate is much gentler. The second photo shows severe deterioration of a larger size decking board in a large deck in Australia. However, very few of the boards as a whole had deteriorated, indicating care has to be taken to ensure every board is up to grade. The photos were taken by the author.

A Quebec Deck   Deteriorated Decking Board

Sometimes for budgetary reasons treated pine is used as a decking timber. In the case of smaller domestic decks, the same protection as outlined for hardwood decks is required. Where thicker treated pine is used in boardwalks the lower initial cost has to be balanced against the much longer life of the hardwood product. The photo on the next page shows a treated pine boardwalk on the edge of a beach after many years of service. The deterioration is very obvious and the cause is not decay as the timber was preservative treated but solar radiation and weathering. Replacement of boards as and when required is necessary to maintain necessary safety standards. Photo taken by the author.

Damage or Destruction by Fire

Fire is, of course, a major destroyer of timber whether it be in structures built by man or in the forest. The purpose of this section is to give a brief insight into the many factors involved when considering timber and the effects of fire. *Australian Standard 1530* covers the early fire hazard

Deteriorated Pine Boardwalk, Noosa Beach

properties of timber and AS 1720.4 can be applied to determine fire resistance levels (FRLs) for solid timber members. In additio, the NCC BCA deals extensively with this subject, particularly the requirements for the different types of structures whether they be domestic dwellings or buildings classed as 2 to 9 such as offices, schools, aged care buildings, multistory buildings, hospitals etc., and sets out minimum requirements for materials used including timber. There are two categories one for buildings that have a sprinkler system and another where no sprinkler system exists. The building code also requires compliance as regards ignitability index, spread of flame index and smoke developed index for certain types of buildings. There is a variation in the performance of different species with regard to these criteria with denser hardwoods performing better. In any design work it can then be seen how important it is that the *BCA* be studied to ensure compliance in all the various areas of the *Code*. In addition, there are Government regulations covering smoke alarm requirements for domestic dwellings. Unfortunately, a lot of older buildings of various types do not meet the current requirements and fires around Australia still happen daily. In the bushfire season fire also results in the destruction of domestic dwellings. Sadly, the ability of most types of construction including masonry clad buildings offer very little protection against the onslaught of very severe forest fires.

While metals and concrete will not burn timber will. However, under intense heat steel expands appreciably and in the case of beams can push over external walls and cause the building to collapse. On the other hand, timber does not expand when exposed to fire and heat. While smaller cross-section timber will burn readily, large section timber beams can char on the surface and this gives a level of self-insulation while still providing strength. In so doing such beams can provide time for occupants to exit the building.

In assessing the ability of different timber species to resist radiation from fire the term 'critical radiant flux' has been devised and in simple terms this means the timbers ability to resist ignition when subject to intense radiant heat. The higher the figure the greater the resistance.

The assessment of the different species for critical radiant flux is carried out under the *Australian Standard ISO 9293.1*. The longer the species resists the exposure to the radiant heat before ignition takes place the higher the number allocated. Two figures are used 2.2 and over and 4.5 and over. The *BCA* [*Building Code of Australia*] then sets out the minimum required for various elements in the building [floors, walls, ceilings etc., in different areas for the different classes of building. There are two divisions those fitted with an approved sprinkler system and those without. Thirty-five of the more common Australian species plus the imported hardwood merbau [*kwila*] have been assessed and they are listed below.

Species with a critical radiant flux of 4.5 or over

Beech	Gum River Red	Karri
Blackbutt New England	Gum Spotted	Mahogany Red
Blackwood	Gum Sugar	Merbau
Bloodwood red	Gum Yellow	Pine White Cypress
Box Brush	Ironbark Grey	Tallowwood
Box Grey	Ironbark Red	Turpentine
Gum Southern Blue	Jarrah	Wattle Silver

Species with a critical radiant flux of 2.2 and less than 4.5

Ash Alpine	Gum Sydney Blue	Pine Celery Top
Ash Mountain	Gum Manna	Pine Radiata
Ash Silvertop	Gum Rose	Stringybark Brown
Blackbutt	Gum Shining	
Brown Barrel	Messmate	

Chapter 8: Working With Timber

The purpose of this chapter is to give some simple explanations about the regular tools used in working with timber and procedures used in such operations as sawing, dressing and machining, etc. There are many terms used in each of these operations that it is handy to know, particularly for those who are new to these activities and have limited knowledge and experience. The professional wood worker will undoubtedly be familiar with most of these terms. There is also some information on how certain properties of timber can affect these operations. At the end of the chapter there is a short section on health and safety as regards sawdust and sander dust.

There is a great range of literature covering the subject of the use of tools in working with timber ranging from books and wood working magazines to the instructions that go with the wide range of machines that are now available. Naturally these instructions should be carefully studied before using any specific machine. The procedures have moved on greatly since all timber was sawn, machined and profiled by hand.

In Chapter 2, on Timber Mill Operations, an insight was given into much the same subjects viz. sawing, dressing and machining plus drying but this involved the large-scale operations of taking the log from the forest and transforming it into commercial timber products. Large sophisticated machinery is involved and much of it now, especially in the milling of plantation pines, is computer controlled. Larger scale joinery works also now have sophisticated machinery. This short chapter covers the other end of the scale of operations.

Sawing

As a starting point in considering sawing, it is generally understood that there is a basic difference in the sawing operation between sawing along a line parallel to the grain as opposed to cutting across the grain. The first is commonly referred to as rip sawing, the other as cross cutting. In the first the saw is following a line parallel to the trunk of the tree and is slicing through the lengths of the fibres that make up the structure of the tree. In the second the saw is cutting across the fibres and the cell walls. Cutting across the piece of timber at an angle involves a proportion of rip sawing and a proportion of cross cutting, the proportion varying according to the angle. Cutting across the timber fibres in the cell structure of timber offers more resistance than cutting along the lengths of the fibres.

Different tooth profiles have been designed for cross cutting and

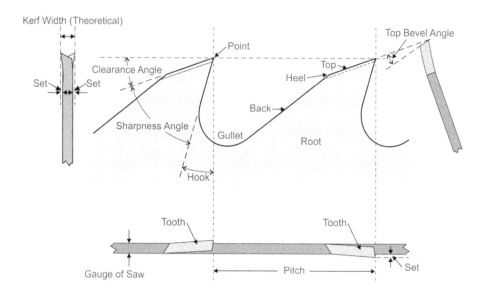

Sawtooth Design

ripping, as well as other profiles to allow for the differences in hardness namely for hard timbers and soft timbers. Using a hand saw designed for ripping for cross cutting will give a very untidy finish and using a cross cut saw for ripping will normally be slow and tedious. In the case of most hand-held circular saws for general purpose work, the tooth profiles are a compromise so that they can be used for hardwood and softwood and also for rip and crosscut sawing. Obviously, they do not give optimum performance in all the different options. With hand saws commonly different saws exist for different applications.

Saw Metallurgy and Teeth Design

Over the years the steel used in saws, the design of the teeth and the use of tungsten carbide tips have come a long way and the rapid blunting and need to frequently sharpen have been greatly reduced. Special high-speed steels are used either in the saw as a whole, the tooth as a whole or just the tip is specially hardened. Studies have shown that although tungsten tipped saws are able to handle a wider range of timbers without the need for regular sharpening, the high-speed steel saws generally produce a better finish.

As mentioned above, the advent of tungsten carbide tips on circular saws was a significant development. Tungsten carbide is an extremely hard substance [with a hardness of 9, second only to diamond which is graded at 10 on the hardness scale]. The tips used in these saws are usually made by sintering together fine particles of tungsten carbide with particles of cobalt as a binder and then brazing into slots cut into the saw blade. Just as steel saw tips vary greatly in design so carbide tips can vary according to the projected use. As with steel teeth the design also ensures the width of the cut is sufficient to prevent the blade binding in the cut. As with all saws and tools in general, the product can vary in quality according to the price paid.

Commonly Used Terms with Saws

Some of the basic terms that are used in referring to saws are listed below. While the terms are illustrated on a simple hand saw they equally apply to circular saws, band saws, frame saws and radial arm saws used for docking.

- Gauge: thickness of the saw itself
- Kerf: width of the sawcut
- Set: difference between the Kerf and the Gauge [i.e., the clearance that prevents the saw binding in the sawcut]
- Hook: Angle from face of tooth to vertical [see diagram]
- Pitch: The distance from one tooth tip to the next
- Gullet: Space left between a line from one tooth tip to the next tooth tip and the back of the saw. It allows the sawdust to get away.
- Bevel: A deviation from the line of the back of the tooth near the tip of the tooth [see diagram] Used to reduce sharpness of the tooth and in so doing reduce the frequency of sharpening. It also increases the strength of the tooth.

Dressing or Planing

For its use in this chapter dressing refers to producing a smooth surface on a sawn board. Some producers and suppliers also use the terms D4S or DAR which mean dressed on four sides or dressed all round. Associated with planers is the term Edger. This is a very similar machine which trues up, i.e., gives parallel edges and produces a smooth surface on the edges of timber. It is very useful where timber is being glued together on the edges, e.g., in the production of table tops. It is more common to joinery shops.

The two main materials used for cutter blades are high speed steel HSS and carbide. HSS is a steel alloy containing in addition to the iron the elements carbon, tungsten, molybdenum, vanadium, cobalt and chromium. Carbide is a material that, as mentioned above, ranks second only to diamond in the scale of hardness. The carbide particles are embedded in a tough metallic binder for use in cutter blades. A range of different carbide products is available. Carbide is used on very hard timbers as well as on particleboard and laminated timbers. With all planers if a good finish is to be achieved all the cutting blades have to be kept sharp regardless of the material used.

Planers vary in size from a fixed machine where boards can be fed through to hand portable machines commonly used on construction sites and by many home handymen. Planers are also commonly used to reduce the thickness. Normally the cutters work in a counter rotation mode i.e., the cutting motion of the tool is opposite to the direction of feed of the timber being machined. The essential principal of the operation is that the rotating cutting blade first penetrates into the wood and when it reaches the centre point it lifts and comes out. Alternatively, the rotation may be synchronous where the cutting motion and direction of feed are the same. In counter rotation the chip breaks away before the knife exits. This leads to longer tool life and less power but there is the risk of tear

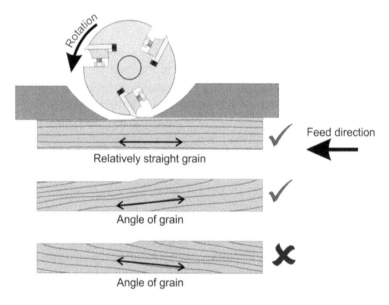

Types of Cutting by Planers

out. With synchronous rotation the risk of tear out is minimal even with twisted and spiral grain timber. However, tool life is lower and power consumption is higher. This type of rotation is necessary with particle board to prevent chip out. The following drawing illustrates three types of cutting in relation to grain direction. Number 1 is cutting 'with' the grain, number 2 is cutting 'into' the grain and number 3 is cutting 'out' of the grain. The grain direction can normally be seen by looking at the side of a piece of timber.

The number of elliptical cuts per centimeter is the concept used to determine the smoothness of the finish. It is controlled by many factors. These include the speed of rotation, speed of feeding of the timber and the number of knives on the cutter block. The depth of the cut also involves the accuracy of setting of the blades. Knife cuts per 30mm is criteria used in practice for determining smoothness. The more knife cuts per 30mm the smoother is the finish. For very smooth finishes more than 25 knife cuts per 30mm is required. Such a smooth finish is necessary where the final painting or clear finishing of the timber is to be carried out without major sanding. Most internal joinery falls into this category. For example, the relevant Australian Standard 2796.1 covering Sawn and Milled Hardwood for lining boards, joinery, mouldings and dressed boards specifies that cutter marks must exceed 15 per 30mm. However, for flooring and decking where such a high degree of smoothness is not required the specification is a minimum of 10 cutter marks per 30mm. With flooring, of course, subsequent sanding is carried out after laying.

Some common terms used in describing planers are as follows:

- *Cutter Blade*: the rotating knife that shaves the timber and gives the smooth surface
- *Cutter Block*: The steel support for the blade
- Other terms used include *sharpness angle* and the *cutting bevel angle* where a bevel is cut to reduce the sharpness and give longer life to the knife before having to regrind.
- *Jointing* is a term that refers to ensuring all the blades project the same so that one or more blades are not carrying out more of the cutting. It is carried out by rotating the blades against a fixed grinder that can be mounted on the machine. However, if the blades have been correctly set up in the first place little or no grinding should be necessary. This process is normally only used in large scale planning machines.

Most planers have a 30-degree grinding angle [the sharpness] and this has been found suitable for softwoods and softer hardwoods. However, with the denser hardwoods if the angle is too acute there is insufficient strength in the cutting edge and the blade quickly loses sharpness. Grinding a face bevel of about 10 degrees [giving a grinding angle of 40 degrees] is a relatively easy way of increasing the cutting angle [or in other terms reducing the sharpness.] This then improves the surface finish and keeps the blade sharper longer. This face bevel is not the depth of the grinding angle only the depth of the chip. However, for general purpose use and away from the large-scale manufacturing plant and joinery shop, different manufacturers have worked out their own preferences for cutting angle based on their experience and the timbers they are regularly dressing. It is usually a compromise.

Other Factors Affecting Planing and Dressing

While grain direction, wavy and twisted grain plus hardness require necessary steps to be taken to ensure a smooth finish, another factor is the incidence of surface knots which can cause chip out giving a rough finish. These problems can be minimized by greatly reducing the depth of the cut.

The presence of some other substances in the cell structure particularly in the truewood can also affect the planing operation. Also, excessive amounts of gummy substances particularly in some conifers can deposit on the cutters and affect the operation and necessitate frequent cleaning. Some timbers contain silica in the cell structure and this can rapidly blunt the cutters. Typical examples of this are the hardwoods brush box and turpentine, the cabinet timber walnut and sometimes in teak. The use of carbide tipped cutters if regularly dressing these timbers can assist.

While all of these points are valid in smaller scale timber operations the general range of planers available, as pointed out above, do involve a compromise in cutter design to handle as many circumstances as possible. However, if it is known that certain types of timber will regularly be used it is a good idea to keep some of the points above in mind when selecting a machine. For example, if most of the work involves hard dense timber a greater cutting angle or tungsten carbide tipped cutters should be considered when purchasing a machine.

Cutter for Moulding
Photo courtesy of Weinig Australia

Machining [Moulding]

In this section of the chapter, machining is taken to refer to the more complicated process of producing special profiles which can range from tongue and groove for flooring, internal timber paneling and profiled external cladding. Also, the various designs of internal mouldings such as architraves require special profiles. Such equipment is usually confined to major manufacturing plants with highly specialized machinery and a great deal of computer control so that it is not proposed to cover moulding operations in detail. The essential difference from planing is that the cutting edge of the knife in used in moulding operations is profiled to produce the required shape of the moulding being produced. The diagram below illustrates a typical cutter head and knife.

In the early days of producing mouldings, specially designed wooden hand planes were used for small scale work [a time consuming process].

Routing

Routers have been around for over a hundred years and over that time as expected a great many improvements have been developed and the list of router bits for different operations is enormous. Routers are commonly classified by their horsepower with light 0.5 HP machines very suitable for light weight more delicate work. For general purpose work 1HP to 1.5HP routers are common particularly for trades people and keen home handy men. Higher horse power machines have been developed for larger scale heavy continuous production.

The big difference between routers and other machines is the speed of rotation. The typical electric hand drill ranges up to 2500 revolutions per minute. The typical circular saw ranges up to 5500 RPM. Routers can range from 20,000 to 25,000 RPM. While safety is important with all the machines it is even more so with routers.

There are a wide range of routers available. These vary from a simple hand-held plunge router, to ones that can be set up on router tables and to the sophisticated computer-controlled CNC router which can then be programmed to rout to the shape required. The CNC routers now find

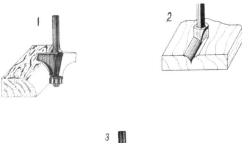

Different Types of Routing

application in cutting out the required shapes for cross laminated timber as for example window and door openings.

For the tradesmen and home handyman, the versatility of the router is invaluable. As regards router bits the range is immense and carbide tipped bits are common and provide a long life against wear. Illustrated are just a few of the many types of bits available. There is also a sketch showing some different types of routing illustrating the flexibility of routers. Sketch 1 on the previous page shows a carbide tipped ball bearing piloted bit. Sketch 2 shows a point cutting quarter round used for decorating, carving and beading and Sketch 3 shows a dovetail bit available with various degree angled edges.

Turning

This refers to the use of a lathe to produce a wide range of crafted articles. This could involve a home craftsman who has his own lathe or it could be part of a larger group either specializing in turning or carrying out a wide range of crafts involving wood. One of the most important aspects in turning is the selection of suitable species having the desired colour, grain and figure for the project in mind. Once the species is selected, then the available source of supply might mean that the timber is seasoned or unseasoned and it may contain untreated sapwood. Each of these possibilities then leads to important factors that have to be considered.

Seasoned Timber

Ideally seasoned timber with a moisture content around 12% is the best option. This is because of the shrinkage, splitting, checking and change in dimension that may occur when unseasoned timber dries down to be in equilibrium with the atmosphere is avoided. However, there are a few hardwoods where shrinkage is relatively low so using them in the unseasoned state is not a real problem. One example is kwila and its related species merbau. Softwoods commonly shrink only around 5% from green to dry so shrinkage much less of a problem. The table at the end of this section sets out shrinkage data for a number of popular species.

Unseasoned Timber

Some of the benefits of using unseasoned timber for turning are as follows:

Easier to Work

When working timber whether it be sawing or machining or in this case turning, unseasoned timber is easier to use because seasoning considerably increases the hardness.

Species Availability

A lot of very desirable species can only be accessed in the unseasoned state.

If a decision is taken to work with unseasoned timber it is wise to check on the shrinkage rate from green to dry of the species selected so that an estimation of dimension change of the turned article once it seasoned can be calculated and whether this might become a problem. Shrinkage data is included for some of the more common species favoured by turners in the list at the end of this section. A larger list of species is included in the Appendices. It is also wise to remember that shrinkage parallel to length of a piece of timber is negligible. Reference to the relevant section in Chapter 6 gives the relation between shrinkage of timber in different directions.

It is quite practicable to air dry some species. This involves stacking the boards so that air can circulate through and around the boards and the stack. The stack obviously must be protected from the rain but still be in a position to get good air flow. In chapter 3 there is more detail on the methods used commercially for air drying with photographs of stacks. How long this takes is the controlling factor in deciding whether to consider air drying. Under favourable conditions 25mm thick boards of lower density [under 650kg/m3] should be able to be air dried in two to three months. However denser hardwoods such as the eucalypts can take 9 months or more. In the drying process checking of whether the timber is fully seasoned can be done by progressively weighing a sample board until the weight is constant. In the home situation this can be weighed on the kitchen scales. If access to a moisture meter is available this is much easier and more accurate way to check on the progress.

When it comes to air seasoning of larger section timber it can take a long time. Most 50 mm thick hardwoods can take years not months, so to do it yourself is only an option if time is not a problem. Also, in this drying process there is the risk of downgrade in the form of serious cracks and splits with the possible loss of valuable timber.

After checking the above information, it is obvious that seasoning the timber is not easy and the only practical option often available is for the turner to work with timber in the unseasoned state especially if larger section sizes are required. However, until the project gets underway some precautions can be taken to minimize any splits or checks by applying liberal coats of products which when applied to the surface and particularly the end grain slow the rapid drying out of the timber. Small pieces can obviously be wrapped in plastic. After the finished article is produced it also then has to be carefully seasoned to prevent splitting and checking.

Reading Chapter 6 on timber and moisture can provide a lot of useful information on shrinkage Including the moisture content that green timber has to dry to before shrinkage begins to occur.

Timber Containing Sapwood

While sapwood has the same strength as the truewood [heartwood], if seasoned hardwood is to be turned and any sapwood that is present has not been treated, it can be attacked by the lyctus [powder post] borer. The lyctus borer does not attack timbers classified as softwoods such as pine because of the different cell structure. If unseasoned timber is used the attack will occur once the turned article dries out. The damage is always severe with most of the sapwood reduced to powder. This borer is not found throughout Australia and the various Forestry Departments can advise on this but it is found in Queensland and NSW. While some species of hardwood are not attacked many of the hardwoods favoured for turning are. The list below sets out those timbers susceptible to attack. If the unlikely event that the finished article is to be placed in an exterior fully exposed situation decay may occur. Reference to Chapter 7 on fungal attack sets out the necessary information on this matter including timbers with high natural decay resistance.

With the softwoods the sapwood can be attacked by the furniture beetle [anobium species] However, the source of the insect is from furniture or other local infestation and it is completely different from the lyctus borer which flies in from the surrounding locality.

In addition to lyctus there are other beetles which can cause problems. Chapter 7 also contains a lot of information about the beetles that attack seasoned timber and the necessary steps to prevent attack.

Data On Common Timbers Used In Or Suitable For Turnng

Common Name	Botanical Name	Colour	Hardness	Lyctus Susceptible	% Shrinkage Green to Dry
Ash Crows	*Flindersia sp*	white/cream	hard	S	4.2
Ash Silver	*Flindersia sp*	white/cream	medium	S	5.4
Ash Alpine	*Eucalyptus spp*	light brown	medium	S	8.5
Beech Myrtle	*Nothofagus*				
	Cunninghamii	pink/brown	medium	S	6.8
Beech white	*Gmelina spp*	creamy brown	medium	S	3.5
Brush Box	*Lophostemon sp*	Med Brown	hard	NS	9.7
Camphor Laurel	*Cinnamonum sp*	Med Brown	medium	S	N/A
Cedar Red *Qld*	*Toona australis*	Red	very soft	S	4.1

Cypress Pine	*Callitris colu-mellaris*	straw/white	medium	NS	2.5
Maple Qld	*Flindersia sp*	light brown	soft	NS	7.2
Mulga	*Acacia aneura*	brown	very hard	NS	N/A
Oak U.S & U.K	*Quercus spp*	light brown	med hard	S	5.0
Oak Silky Nth	*Cardwellia sublimis*	light brown	medium	S	4.7
Pine Hoop/Bunya	*Auracaria spp*	straw/white	soft	NS	3.8
Pine Huon	*Dacrydium sp*	straw/white	soft	NS	
Pine Radiata	*Pinus radiata*	straw/white	soft	NS	5.1
Rosewood Imported	*Pterocarpus sp*	Red	medium	S	4.9
Spotted Gum	*Corymbia maculata*	brown	hard	S	6.1
Walnut Qld	*Endriandra palmerstonii*	brown	hard	NS	4.6

NOTES: Brush Box and Qld. Walnut contain silica which can blunt tools. Tangential shrinkage figures are tabled – radial are roughly 50% of tangential.

Timber and Health

As all the activities involved in working with timber normally produce sawdust and sander dust in the finishing process a short section on the matter of any effects on the health of those involved was felt to be appropriate. This concern for health is common in all construction processes and care needs to be taken to prevent health hazards arising in the procedures involved in the use of the other materials as well as timber. In previous times large numbers of workers ultimately suffered fatal consequences when working with asbestos cement. Sadly, the dangers were not known. Even today where renovations are occurring in structures containing asbestos cement strict safety methods are necessary. More recently the need to avoid breathing the dust from grinding and shaping stone bench tops has received publicity and methods to prevent lung damage from inhaling silicon dioxide [sand] in the stone are necessary.

While wood is a relatively friendly substance with which to work there is still the need to take sensible care when working with it. Firstly, and obviously sawdust has to be kept out of the eyes as it can damage the surface of the eye. What steps are necessary depends on the degree of risk from different operations. Secondly inhaling sawdust needs to be kept out of the lungs by the use of good quality respirators when carrying out sanding and sawing. Paper masks that do not completely filter out the fine dust are not the best solution. In the workplace larger machines should be fitted with efficient dust extraction systems. If dusts enter the lungs, they can then interchange with other parts of the body including the blood stream and central nervous system. The most dangerous particles are very fine from 5 microns to 25microns in size as they are more able to get past the body's natural defences. [Normal copy paper is about 25 microns thick.] Sanding in particular produces these very fine particles. It is also wise to minimize skin exposure.

A similar problem exists with sawdust greater than 25 microns in size and shavings but to a lesser extent. Apart from causing lung problems the main problems that occur are dermatitis and skin irritation. It is also well established medically that the reactions of individuals varies considerably. Those subject to asthma need to take extra precautions to prevent breathing in dust from various timber operations. However, the ultimate problem is a medical one and the medical profession and State Health Departments should be sought for information and advice on any workplace problems.

Many years ago, Dr. Eleanor Bolza of the CSIRO extensively researched the subject particularly from the aspect of identifying the chemical substances liable to cause problems and checking the differences with the different timber species. This not only covered the more common Australian species but an extensive range of overseas timbers. Very few of these imported species are available in Australia today. Most of this work is still being used as reference material as the CSIRO have not updated the information. The following list covers some of the more common Australian and a few imported species with the health hazard that may occur.

Species	Health Hazards That May Occur
Victorian Ash/ Messmate	Dermatitis, nose, eye and throat irritation
Tasmanian blackwood	Dermatitis, nose, eye and throat irritation
Crows Ash	Dermatitis
Oregon	Dermatitis, nose, eye and throat irritation
Grey Box [*e.hemiphloia*]	Eczema, nose irritation
Jarrah	Nose, eye and throat irritation
Meranti	Nose, eye and throat irritation and dermatitis
Mulga	Nose, eye and throat irritation headache
Red Cedar	Severe reaction to dust including dermatitis, headaches, giddiness, asthma, etc.,
Spotted Gum	Dermatitis
Western Red Cedar	Dermatitis, wheezing, etc., plus sensitizati once exposed. This species contains toxic resins.

While not listed, the breathing in of dust from species that contain silica should be strictly avoided. Examples of such species include brush box, turpentine, walnut and teak.

No attempt has been made to cover operations involving the use of preservative treated timbers. The use of the chemicals involved in preservation comes under the control of the Australian Pest and Veterinary Authority [APVA] but obviously this is not meant to handle health issues that might occur with dust from untreated timber operations. It is considered good practice to avoid inhaling any dust from preservative treated wood. The elimination of arsenic in all but the highest level of preservation has also removed exposure to a dangerous substance. One approved preservative that is usually hand applied is creosote which has a severe effect on the skin and great care by the use of protective clothing, gloves, etc., is advisable in its use. As mentioned above the ultimate referee on the above subject rests with the State Health Departments and the medical profession who need to be consulted if problems arise. The above information is given to provide some useful background information.

Chapter 9: Fabricated Timber Products

This chapter includes information on the following:

- Plywood
- Decorative Veneers
- Particleboard
- Fibreboard
- Hardboard
- Bamboo Board Products

Introduction

All of the above products extend the use of timber into other applications by the use of synthetic and natural resins. An essential element in this process is the turning the solid timber into veneers, wood chips or fibres. It also results in the more efficient use of the timber resource and minimizes wastage. While paper is also a product largely derived from timber as its source material, it is not proposed to cover this product in this chapter.

Plywood

Plywood was produced for many years before the advent of particleboard and fibreboard. It provides a structurally strong seasoned product in sheet form. It is thus a very useful product in the building and furniture industries. While, particularly in the furniture industry, solid timber boards can be edge glued to provide sheets as for example in table tops, this is practically very difficult where a thin low thickness sheet is required.

Plywood will be covered under the following headings:

- Manufacture including types of glues
- Grading and Strength of plywood
- Movement with moisture change
- Durability
- Finishing
- Main Types of Plywood

Manufacture

The main steps involved are:

- Production of Veneer
- Lay up and gluing of the veneers

Veneer Production

Veneers are the thin sheets of timber that are required for the production of plywood. They are produced by the rotary peeling of a debarked log. Rotary peeling involves rotating the log against a fixed knife. The length of the veneer is then dependent on the length of the knife or the length of the log. The width of the veneer produced can be varied by where the continuous length of veneer issuing from the knife is cut [clipped]. Softwoods such as radiata pine are easily peeled, but hardwoods especially the denser species need preconditioning in hot water or by steaming to soften the timber so that it can be satisfactorily peeled. Lower density hardwoods such as meranti are relatively easy to peel. As there are different plywood designs dependent on the projected use, the thickness of the veneer is adjusted to meet design layup. Rotary peeled veneer thicknesses range from 0.9mm to 3.0mm. It should be noted that veneers required as decorative overlays require different methods of production and this subject is covered in the section on veneers. The following photograph shows veneer issuing from a lathe after rotary peeling.

Peeling of Veneers

Drying and Grading

After peeling the veneers are fed into a continuous dryer so that all veneers are at the same moisture content. This prevents moisture stresses occurring which can then cause the finished plywood to warp. The end moisture content is determined by the glue being used and is normally 12% or less. After issuing from the dryer the veneers are graded according to the type of plywood for which the veneer is intended and also whether the veneer is to be face, back or internal. The highest-grade veneers are generally reserved for face veneers.

Veneer Width

Normally the width and length of rotary peeled veneers can be produced to suit the size of the plywood being laid up. In laying up veneers to produce plywood, with very few exceptions, the grain direction of each veneer is at right angles to the veneer on either side of it and this cross lamination gives the plywood strength and stiffness in both the length and width. Normally for the face and back veneers plus the centre veneer the grain direction is parallel to the length of the sheet. Therefore, for a given size of sheet of plywood it is necessary to produce two sets of veneers, firstly those where the grain direction is parallel to the length of the plywood sheet [the long bands] and secondly those where the grain direction is parallel to the width of the sheet [the cross bands].

Grading of the Veneers during Plywood Production

Just as sawn timber has to be graded so also there is a need to grade veneers before they are laid up into plywood. This is because the veneer grade must meet the requirements of the end product being manufactured. The different grades of veneer are covered in more detail in the section that follows on exterior grade plywood.

Tight and Loose Veneer Sides

Whether rotary peeling or slicing the veneer produced has what is called a tight and loose side. The tight side is the one produced next to the knife. The texture on the loose side is more open than on the tight side. It will thus absorb more finish or stain or whatever is coating the surface. In rotary peeling the side away from the knife has to flatten out and expand to form a flat sheet of veneer and this opens up the surface to give the loose side. Normally it is usual to expose the tight sides on the face and back. For the inner veneers tight sides are usually glued to loose sides but it is not mandatory. However in the use of veneers in decorative products it can be of significance. This again will be covered in the section on veneers further in the chapter.

Veneer Thickness

The veneer thickness is varied to suit the plywood to be produced. It commonly can vary from 0.5mm to 4mm. As the glue is costly the less veneers used means the lower the cost of the plywood. On the other hand, with decorative veneers thinner veneers are produced to maximize recovery from precious resources. However, all this is governed by the design of the plywood sheet to give the required structural strength for the application.

With veneers used to lay up into plywood flooring the selected species used for the face veneer needs to be 2.5mm to 4mm to give the ability to sand the face after installation. The thicker veneer also gives better resistance to indentation from high heeled shoes if the plywood is destined for use as the finished floor.

Lay Up and Gluing of the Veneers

Lay up of a sheet of plywood requires the assembly of the necessary number of veneers with alternate long bands [grain oriented to the length of the sheet] interspersed with crossbands [grain oriented to the width of the sheet]. Except for special purpose plywood there is always an odd number of veneers in a sheet of plywood with, as mentioned above, the face, back and centre veneers being long bands. So the terms 3 ply, 5 ply, 7 ply etc., are often used. The long bands give the sheet of plywood strength in length of the sheet, the crossbands give strength across the width.

In typical procedure the crossbands are fed through a glue roller with glue applied to both surfaces. The assembly of veneers is then cold pressed [prepressed] to transfer the glue from the spread to the unspread veneer. The assembly of veneers is then fed between two platens of a hot press commonly 2.4 metres by 1.2 metres in size where the glue is cured under heat and pressure. The issuing sheet is inspected to ensure complete gluing of all veneers before being sent for trimming to the exact size. The sheet may or may not be sanded according to its final required use.

Glues Used

When plywood was first manufactured glues such as casein, animal glues and others were used for bonding the veneers together. Most had little resistance to delamination in the presence of water. With advent of the modern urea formaldehyde, phenol formaldehyde and resorcinol formaldehyde glues, better more reliable and durable exterior bonds can be achieved. Which type of glue is used depends on the final application and in particular whether firstly it is for interior or exterior application and secondly whether long term structural properties are required.

Glues used for interior applications generally have limited resistance to water and the veneers will delaminate if the plywood becomes wet. Commonly urea formaldehyde glues are used and, to reduce cost, some manufacturers may 'extend' the glue by adding in fillers.

Glues for exterior or structural applications such as flooring and form plywood are classed asdurable and so the plywood will not delaminate if exposed to wet conditions. They are commonly referred to as having an A bond. The glue used for exterior plywood is commonly phenol formaldehyde. Although the glue is not soluble in water this does not mean the plywood will not absorb water if exposed to wet [external] conditions. The misconception that the plywood will not absorb water comes from the common practice of referring to this plywood as 'waterproof' plywood. The face and back veneers absorb water and although the glueline is waterproof water is absorbed in to the interior veneers through the edges of the sheet.

Grading and the Strength Properties of Plywood

Veneer Grading

When purchasing structural plywood, terms such as CD frequently show up on the branding or purchase paperwork. Some buyers have no idea what this means, others understand it refers to the veneers used and the more informed understand it refers to the grading of the face and back veneers. To understand it better, reference has to be made to the *Australian Standard 2269* for structural plywood which sets out the limits for the natural defects such as knots, holes, etc. that occur. The *Standard* defines five grades which are as follows.

A   A high grade appearance grade suitable for clear finishing
B   An appearance grade suitable for painting
C   A nonappearance grade with a solid surface
D   A nonappearance grade with permitted open imperfections
S   An appearance grade where certain characteristics are specially negotiated for aesthetic appeal.

So the commonly used CD exterior plywood has a C grade veneer on the face and a D grade veneer on the back. [refer the above definitions to assess what to expect]

Veneer Grading Defects

Veneer grading is covered by an Australian Standard which sets out the incidence and limits of natural defects [e.g knot and hole size] and so can affect the practicability in use and also the strength just as occurs with solid timber. The main defects that can occur are:

- Bark, Gum and Resin pockets
- Unfilled holes and splits
- Gum Veins
- Knots
- Stains, glue bleed through and resin streaks
- Surface roughness

For maximum strength along the length of the sheet the grain should be exactly parallel to the length of the sheet. This of course rarely happens in practice and a specification for structural veneers as to how much deviation from being parallel to the edge in the lengthwise direction has been set. For structural veneers this is 1 in 7. This means, in the case of the 2400 mm length, the grain can deviate by 2400 divided by 7 or 340mm. Or when measuring the angle it is 90 degrees divided by 7 which equals 13 degrees so the angles as measured has to be above 90 minus 13 or 77 degrees. The same applies to the cross bands but the calculations have to be adjusted to 900mm or 1200mm the width of the sheet. As mentioned previously the less the slope of grain the greater the strength.

Very briefly the grading is as follows

- A-Grade Veneer: The only imperfections allowed are up to 4mm diameter knots and only 4 per sheet and slight roughness. However filling of very small holes and splits is allowed.
- B-Grade Veneer: Very similar to A grade but slightly larger knots [25mm] Also there is no limit on variations in colour
- C-Grade Veneer: The grading is less restrictive than A or B grades with solid knots and filled holes allowed. However bark, resin and gum pockets and unfilled holes and splits are not allowed.
- D-Grade Veneer: As this is used on the back and in the interior veneers of the sheet most of the restrictions not permitted in the above three grades are allowed but the veneer has to be structurally sound.

Strength Properties

Timber can be considered a non-homogeneous substance. This means it has different properties in different directions and this is due to its cell structure. With solid timber the greatest strength lies in the direction of the grain and is lower tangentially across the grain or radially at right angles to the grain. With steel and aluminum which are homogeneous the strength is equal in all directions and the strength in any direction is governed by the dimensions in that direction. Plywood which is also a non-homogeneous product is different to solid timber. When designing structures using plywood sheets consideration has to be given to the number of veneers and the plywood thickness, the thickness and placement of the veneers [the face and back veneers contribute the most to the strength of the plywood] and the veneer species. Obviously, hardwood veneers have greater strength than softwood veneers. The centre veneer is considered the neutral axis with expansion on one side and compression on the other as the load is applied.

As compared to solid timber there is a difference with plywood where the cross banding of the veneers in its construction means that the strength is evened out in both directions with a reduction in strength in a length wise direction [due to the cross bands] and an increase in strength across the sheet due to the incidence of the cross bands.

Another feature of plywood is its strength to weight ratio compared to other sheet materials. In World War 2 the Allied Mosquito bomber and the Japanese Zero fighter were largely constructed of plywood due to this high strength to weight ratio. One of the reasons for the use of plywood was the limited availability of aluminum. There are many construction applications where this feature can be used such as box beams, folded roof plates and other stressed skin panel applications plus of course all kinds of flooring applications and shuttering for concrete slabs when used for laying the concrete in floors above the ground.

Designing structures requires the use of basic engineering data such as the modulus of elasticity [E], the moment of inertia [I] and other data. Fortunately, most of this design work for plywood used in common building applications has been done. As an example, tables exist for the different thicknesses of plywood required for flooring application covering different spans between support points. Informed plywood suppliers usually have copies of these tables. Alternatively, the Engineered Wood Products Association of Australia [EWPAA] can suggest possible sources of tables. For any special design needs there is a need to call on the services of a qualified timber engineer or refer to the EWPAA for guidance.

Resistance to Splitting

Another feature with the use of plywood is its resistance to splitting. Straight grained solid timber splits readily if nailed or screwed close to the edge because of the cleavage force exerted exceeds the strength across the grain. However, with plywood due to the cross banding of veneers in the manufacture giving strength in this direction, nailing or screwing much closer to the edge is possible.

Movement of Plywood with Moisture Change

Because of the cross banding in plywood movement with changes in moisture content is minimal. Why this happens is explained below.

There is an essential difference with regard to moisture content between plywood and solid timber on one hand, and particleboard and fibreboard on the other. Both plywood and solid timber will expand with increase in moisture content but both will then shrink if the moisture content is reduced i.e., the process is reversible. This is not the case with normal particleboard and fibreboard. Increase in moisture content increases the dimensions and this is permanent. Subsequent reduction in moisture content will not result in shrinkage. In normal internal situations increases and decreases in moisture content are not great so increases and decreases in dimensions are minimal. However, in some situations this can be a problem. However, it has been considerably reduced by the production of high moisture resistant products for use in situations where damp conditions exist, as for example in cabinetry for bathrooms and laundries. Particleboard flooring is another example where high moisture resistant resins and other products like wax are used in the manufacture to resist moisture problems in exposed external conditions where a high moisture resistant product is necessary.

As explained in the earlier chapter 6 on timber movement shrinkage or expansion along the direction of the grain, normally the length is minimal and is roughly 1/100 of that across the grain. With plywood as the lengths of the veneers are alternately at right angles to each other, expansion or shrinkage across the veneers is resisted by the adjoining lengthwise veneer. There is some slight variation according to the thickness of the plywood and in turn the number of plies, the species used and the moisture range. The following table gives the approximate movement that can occur and this is very low. The figures are for where the grain of the face and back veneers is parallel to the length of the sheet.

	Thickness	Moisture Change per 1% Range	moisture change	Moisture Range	Change per 1% moisture change
Along the length	6mm	12% to 17%	0.014%	5% to saturated	0.011% av.
Across the width	6mm	12% to 17%	0.021%	5% to saturated	0.011% av.
Along the length	12mm	12% to 17%	0.009%	5% to saturated	0.010% av.
Across the width	12mm	12% to 17%	0.008%	5% to saturated	0.010% av.
Along the length	17mm	12% to 17%	0.009%	5% to saturated	0.011% av.
Across the width	17mm	12% to 17%	0.010%	5% to saturated	0.011% av.

The figures given are averages to use as the changes with increasing moisture content are dependent on the veneer thicknesses used and the plywood construction itself.

It is of interest to illustrate the use of the above data and also to compare the expansion in width of a 1200 mm wide 17mm thick plywood sheet with a piece of solid timber. The following data will be used.

- Solid timber – 130mm wide x 19mm thick piece of hardwood
- Unit tangential movement – 0.37% per 1% rise in moisture content [Chapter 7 explains unit tangential movement]
- Rise in moisture content – 13%
- Increase in width – 130mm x 13 degrees rise x 0.37% = 6.2mm
- Expansion in width of 2400 x 1200 sheet of plywood 1200mm x 0.011 % x 13 degrees rise = 1.7mm [from above tables]

From this it can be seen that a sheet just over nine times wider than the solid timber expands by just over one quarter of the solid timber.

However, while there is negligible increase in the length of solid timber with increasing moisture content there would have been a 3mm increase in the length of sheet in the above example. The differences are due to the cross lamination of the plywood. Therefore, it is necessary when laying sheets of plywood that a small allowance be made for this small expansion in length and width.

This also does have implications in laying strip flooring made using plywood with a thicker hardwood veneer on the surface. At the end of each strip a small expansion allowance has to be made to cover length wise movement of the plywood. The pieces cannot be butted up as is the practice with solid timber strip flooring.

Normal good floor laying practice requires that flooring be laid with a moisture content midway between expected highs and lows of atmospheric moisture conditions namely from very dry conditions to the wet rainy conditions. Therefore, the extreme case used to calculate and illustrate the difference in the movement of plywood and solid timber flooring should not exist in practice. However, the appreciable differences in movement with changes in moisture content across the widths between plywood and solid timber still exist regardless of the moisture increase or decrease.

Durability of Plywood

When plywood is used externally and subject to rain and moisture its resistance to fungal attack or decay depends mainly on three factors

- the durability rating of the timber used to make the veneers
- whether or not the veneers or plywood have been preservative treated
- the degree of exposure, i.e., is the plywood only wet occasionally [as in severe storms] or is it fully exposed or used in situations such as form ply where it is frequently being wet. Therefore, these factors have to be assessed in determining if the plywood is to be used in exterior situations.

Ideally, where hardwood veneers are being used and decay resistance is required only high durability veneers should be selected as treatment of the truewood of hardwood is basically not achievable. Thus, it is also necessary to know the species of the hardwood veneers so that the durability can be ascertained.

Preservative treatment of pine veneers is usually to H3 standard which covers exterior out of ground contact. Therefore, the ends of sheets e.g., external cladding must be kept clear of the ground where a higher durability rating is necessary.

The fact that the plywood is branded exterior or marine plywood refers to the resistance of the glue to prevent delamination of the veneers in wet conditions not its resistance to decay. The glueline does help prevent the ingress of water into the internal veneers [not the face or back] but water still penetrates through the edges. If the veneers decay the bond of the glue which depends on sound veneer is destroyed and the plywood delaminates. A case study where this happened is detailed in Chapter 11.

Finishing of Plywood

Plywood can be clear finished, 'natural' or stain-finished or conventionally painted. With each method obviously the recommendations of the individual product being used have to be followed. Plywood is not designed because of the thickness of the surface veneers to be used in external situations unfinished. It has been found that in external applications that acrylic water-based primer should be used instead of commonly used oil-based primers. [e.g., tung oil-based] The latter because of their inability to let the veneer move with alternate drying and wetting leads to extensive surface splitting and checking. For the same reason the finish coats should also be acrylic based. Of course, this problem does not exist in internal applications.

With decorative sliced veneer plywood which are only used in internal situations, as is well known, these are normally clear finished.

Main Types of Plywood

The main types of plywood are

- Structural Plywood [*Standard As/NZS 2269*]
- Exterior Plywood [*Standard As/NZS 2271*]
- Marine Plywood [*Standard As/NZS 2272 /BS 1088*]
- Interior Grade Plywood [*Standard As/NZS 2270*]
- Decorative Plywood
- Structural Grade Plywood [ ]

Structural plywood is an engineered wood product with defined structural characteristics which vary according to the intended use. The normal engineering terms such as modulus of elasticity [MOE], modulus of rupture [MOR] bending strength, tensile strength etc., , are defined for a range of species, thicknesses and constructions. In the product information covering the main applications this engineering has been carried out and the load carrying capacity, strength and stiffness requirements for different situations is available by referring to this product information. Typical applications include:

- Bracing Plywood
- Residential and Industrial flooring

- Plywood for Formwork
- Box Beams

Bracing plywood commonly uses hardwood for the veneers which are of higher strength and also provide increased resistance to decay. Because of its application in providing bracing strength to walls in domestic construction and other building it can be weather exposed for reasonable periods of time until the roof is on and the external cladding is completed. There is thus a potential for decay to occur hence the popularity for the use of higher durability hardwood veneers which also have higher strength. The exterior bond provides long term structural adequacy plus resistance to delamination while weather exposed.

Plywood Flooring

Plywood flooring is used both for domestic applications and commercial and industrial applications. It is grooved along the long edges with a plastic tongue inserted and this tongue provides support between the joists. Flooring is stress graded [F8, F11 and F14] and comes is thicknesses from 12mm and up. Sheet size is commonly 2400mm x 1200mm

There are two main applications, either as a subfloor over conventional bearers and joists or for fixing over concrete to which a decorative floor can then be fixed. In the first application over bearers and joists it can then be used as a working platform for construction of the walls and roof. Thickness ranges from 12mm and up with 17mm being very common and 2400mm x 1200mm the normal size. Although the rotary peeled face veneers of the flooring are selected to be free of major surface defects, they are generally not considered aesthetically acceptable enough for a finished floor. Either a decorative timber floor can be fixed over this subfloor or other floor coverings such as carpet, tiles or vinyl laid. Tables are available from manufacturers and suppliers setting out the maximum allowable spans for different thicknesses. The following table illustrates what is available.

Maximum Joist Spacing (mm)	Grade		
	F8	F 11	F14
	Minimum Thickness Required		
400	12	12	12
450	14	13	12.5
480	15	14	13
600	19.5	18.5	17

The second application is where the flooring is manufactured with a face veneer that is one of a number of species that are regularly used in conventional solid timber flooring. In addition, instead of being in sheet form the plywood is run into floor board widths, tongue and groove edges are machined in and it is frequently supplied prefinished. The face veneer has to have sufficient thickness [3mm to 4mm] to allow for future sanding and polishing. Unlike plywood flooring described in [ii] above these products are commonly supplied in thicknesses from 8mm to 10mm. As such they are strictly an overlay flooring to be fixed to a solid base. Their main advantage is speed and ease of installation plus minimal movement with changing atmospheric moisture conditions. However as pointed out previously expansion joints are also required at the ends of the boards.

Plywood for Formwork [*Australian Standard 6669*]

Plywood for formwork industry requires special construction to cope with the needs of this industry which is involved in laying concrete slabs in medium and high-rise buildings. These include high strength to cope with heavy concrete loads, hardwood face and back veneers to resist the impact of the vibrators used to settle the concrete, a permanent exterior bond and a plastic overlay to allow easy stripping of the sheets after the concrete has set. The robust nature of the plywood construction helps in maximizing the number of times the sheets can be used.

Box Beams

These are specifically designed for a range of different construction situations.

Exterior Grade Plywood [*AS/NZS 2271*]

This is a high strength plywood predominantly bonded with a Type A phenol formaldehyde glue to resist any veneer delamination in the presence of moisture. Pine veneers are frequently the most commonly used veneers because of availability, ease of gluing and lower veneer cost. However, if pine veneers are used in external applications the product does require preservative treatment to prevent decay. In Australia three plantation species viz. radiata, carribean, and slash pine hybrids available but radiata is predominantly used. The quality of the veneers used varies according to the product being produced. For example, the exterior cladding requires an A Grade face and normally a D Grade back veneer. On the other hand CD exterior grade has a C Grade face and a D Grade back veneer.
   Applications include:

  • Exterior cladding: This application does require the plywood to be
    preservative treated to prevent decay. It may have a rough sawn face
    to give a weatherboard appearance and the sheets are also tongue and
    grooved on the edges to provide protection against the ingress of rain.

Exterior finishing should be with acrylic water-based primers and finish coats.

- Landscaping: In this application the product is used for retaining walls, steps and other uses and in ground and out of ground exposure is involved. There are limits on the heights of retaining walls. Appropriate preservative treatment to H4 level is absolutely essential.
- [A general purpose strong plywood with a permanent exterior bond for a multitude of uses such as packaging, furniture and cabinet ware. In addition to CD plywood a BC grade is also available.

Marine Plywood

Marine plywood is another variation of exterior and structural plywood with the same exterior long term structural glue used for bonding the veneers. The essential difference is a specification [*Australian Standard 2272-2006*] that calls for a range of very high face and back grade veneers. Also, the backs and faces of the plywood are sanded ready to facilitate finishing. Although a number of species are specified in the specification the range of species is limited. These veneers are sanded to facilitate painting or polishing. In Australia the most common veneer available is hoop pine.

There is no difference in its resistance to delamination due to water exposure from other types of exterior grade plywood. All have to meet very high specifications. There is also no difference in resistance to decay – the plywood will decay in wet external conditions unless the veneers or the plywood are treated to H3 level. Unfortunately, there is a common misconception that because it is used in marine applications it will not decay in external applications. In the boating industry applications good surface finishes and regular maintenance is always recommended. Keeping the boats out of the water, if possible, particularly if the plywood has not been preservative treated also is a sound practice.

The main use is in the boating industry but marine plywood does find other applications where a structural plywood with good quality faces is required.

Interior Plywood [*AS/NZS 2270*]

Interior plywood is produced using an interior type glue such as urea formaldehyde as it is not being subjected to severe moisture conditions. The more expensive exterior glues are not necessary. This type of plywood is used in a multitude of applications for both domestic and commercial applications. Where once plywood was the only product used, the advent of the more economical particleboard and fibreboard has resulted in greatly diminished usage. However, the greater strength of plywood means it still finds application in the thinner sheet applications.

Normally the product comes with a face free from defects such as splits, knots etc., and both face and back are sanded. As such it can be painted or varnished with a minimum of final sanding.

Decorative Plywood

Decorative plywood is a variation of interior plywood where instead of painting or clear finishing a decorative fancy veneer is applied to the surface. This also means that the surface veneer is 0.5mm thick instead of a conventional plywood thickness selected according to the final plywood thickness. Decorative plywood has long been produced and its application is mainly for a decorative board in interior situations. The selection of a particular species for its colour, grain and other features that will blend in with the other facets of the interior design is all important. Decorative veneers applied to plywood are still in use but other substrates such as particleboard and fibreboard are lower in cost and therefore preferred. Veneered boards applications can range from internal joinery and furniture to walls and ceilings. To balance the sheet and prevent warping the face and back veneers must be of the same thickness.

Plywood Availability

In the preceding section on plywood there is a very large range of different types of plywood produced for a wide range of applications. Most timber merchants, hardware stores and other stock lists do not carry all the products listed. What range of types of plywood they carry is of course based on local demand. Therefore, if the product desired is not available locally it may be necessary to search around for some products. This may necessitate referring to large hardware stores or merchants in the larger centres of population for the product required.

Decorative Veneers

Decorative veneers are produced for use on substrates such as plywood, particle board and fibreboard. While the selected species can be used as solid timber and still is, the use in the form of veneer on board substrates enables interior designers more flexibility and a more economical solution. Importantly it also greatly extends the use of a limited resource. In Australia many of the veneers that were available 50 years ago are no longer available as small forest areas where they could be obtained have been logged out and conservation of the main rain forest areas where some of the much-desired species are available is rigorously enforced. However, veneers from some species such as the Victorian alpine ash and mountain ash are generally available as well as the various varieties of pine. Veneer merchants also source a wide variety of different species from around the world. However, interior décor is a fashion business that changes so demand for different species of veneers also changes.

Production of Veneers

While some species of veneers are able to be peeled, decorative veneers are mainly produced by slicing a timber billet or flitch which is a rectangular section length of timber cut from the log. This may be crown [tangentially] cut, quarter cut or a combination of both as determined by which gives the best desired features. One variation of the crown cut is the cathedral cut where the slicing is carried out to give an inverted V resembling a cathedral spire. This is a popular way to present American White Oak and European Oak.

With most hardwood species it is necessary to first soak the billets in hot water for some time to soften the timber before it can be sliced. The size of the billet is determined by the diameter of the tree trunk. Some, like Victorian Ash, can be large while others like Black Bean [if available] are small. Present day lathes are able to slice the billet at any angle so as to maximize the attractiveness of the grain. The species, of course, is selected according to its known veneer features for the project in mind. The veneers as they come from the slicer are kept in the order of slicing. The following diagram shows the source of a billet in the log.

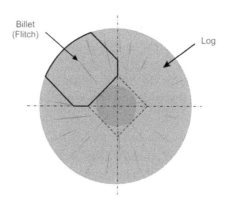

Billet in the Log

The next step involves drying down to about 10% moisture content and then sequentially splicing the veneers together with fine nylon thread to form the layons required for gluing to the selected substrate. Layons are commonly 1200mm wide.

There are three common methods of matching the veneers at the time of splicing. They are:

- Book matching – Where each alternate leaf is turned over like pages in a book
- Slip matching – where each leaf is placed side by side
- Random matching – leaves are selected at random and joined together at random.

Reverse slip match is also sometimes used to give a particular effect with some species of veneers. Each method gives its own particular appearance. Book matching is well liked but can produce a paling fence effect when given a clear finish. The reason for this is that veneers are alternatively laid with the 'tight side' up and then the 'loose side' up. The loose side absorbs more finish and becomes darker in appearance. The subject of tight and loose sides and why it occurs was explained previously in the plywood section.

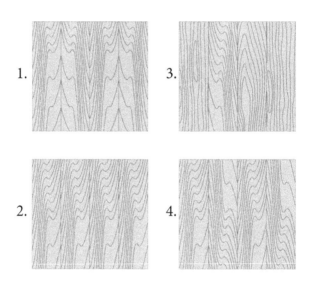

Types of Veneer Matching

The diagram above shows what the effect of each method looks like. As listed, 1 is book match, 2 is slip match, 3 is random match and 4 is reverse slip match.

Australian manufacturers produce an attractive range of veneers including Tasmanian Oak, Blackbutt, Alpine Ash, Mountain Ash, Messmate, Spotted Gum and Hoop Pine. As mentioned above many rainforest species that were popular many years ago are no longer available. In the design process, the veneer selected has to blend in with the rest of the décor. The veneer merchants also handle a great range of veneers from around the world of which American White Oak, European Oak and American Walnut are popular. However, popularity of different veneers is always changing over time and so any listing will therefore also change. The photograph below shows a few veneers from the vast range of veneers available both from Australia manufacturers and internationally. The photos also show the difference in each veneer between quarter cut and crown cut, and which one best suited to the application has to be selected.

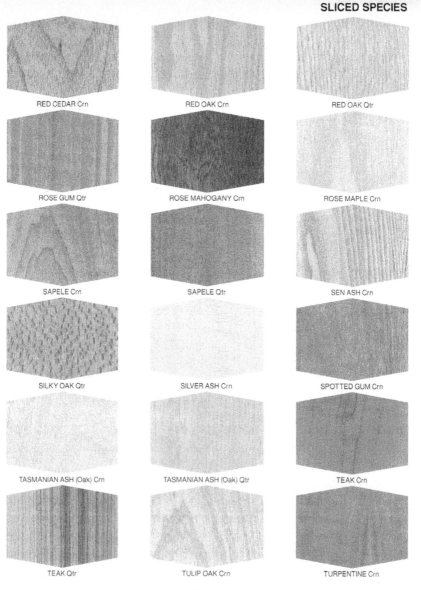

Popular Veneers

Particleboard

Particleboard, which was first produced in Europe in 1941, is a widely used timber sheet material manufactured from wood chips or flakes which are bonded together with a range of suitable resins. Applications range from all kinds of furniture and cabinet work to domestic or commercial flooring. It also provides a ready base for the application of decorative overlays such as melamine [whiteboard], timber veneers and other special overlays.

The manufacture of particleboard involves the production of the chips, blending with the selected resin, forming into a sheet sized matt and then compressing under high pressure and heat to produce the required board thickness. The heat cures the glue. The boards are then trimmed to the required dimensions and fine sanded.

The source of the raw material, normally a softwood such as pine can be from sawmill waste, plantation thinning and other materials such as planer shavings. The chipping of the wood gives a mixture of different sized particles which are screened to give different sized chips from dust and very fine through to relatively coarse. These chips are then dried to 3% to 5% moisture content in a continuous drier before mixing with glue. The most common board is a three-layer board which has a central core of coarser chips with finer chips on each surface. There is also a one-layer board produced in some countries which uses the product from the chipper without screening into various chip sizes. Waferboards, another variation, use very large shavings up to 50mm square with each overlapping the next instead of chips. They are frequently used for walls and ceilings particularly in America and Europe because of the decorative appearance.

The three-layer board consists of a surface layer each side of finer chips with a central core of coarse chips. More glue is required to adequately coat the surfaces of the finer chips normally 10% to 12% of resin and 88% to 90% of chips and this produces a denser stronger surface. The coarser chips used in the interior of the board need less glue [usually 4% to 6%] to cover them. As the resin is the most expensive ingredient the total cost depends on the proportions of fine to coarse chips. The purpose of the surface layer of finer chips with higher resin content is to give a stronger denser surface with increased strength and stability. This surface also is smoother resulting in better paint finish and the better adhesion of other decorative finishes such as veneers and also melamine for 'whiteboard'.

The three main types of synthetic resins used are Urea Formaldehyde [UF], Melamine Formaldehyde [MF] and Phenol Formaldehyde [PF] The urea formaldehyde resins which are the lowest in cost and supply the larger section of the board market where good water resistance is not required. Melamine Formaldehyde is blended with Urea Formaldehyde to produce a high moisture resistant [HMR] board. This is recommended for cabinetware in wet areas such as bathrooms and laundries. The phenol formaldehyde resins which are dark in colour are used where high long-term durability and structural strength plus water resistance are required. For example, this glue is used in the manufacture of particle board flooring.

When interior grade particleboard is exposed to increased moisture conditions up to 20% the linear dimensions [length and width] will increase by 0.03% to 0.06% for every 1% increase in moisture content. The thickness will increase by 0.3% to 0.5% for every 1% increase in moisture content. The considerable difference is due to the way the chips are laid up.

High moisture resistant particle board is produced for situations where it is liable to be exposed to wet conditions. The most typical application is for flooring for domestic construction. In this use it is usually exposed to the weather [rain] until the roof is completed. Other applications include cabinet work in bathrooms and laundries where the humidity is usually high and for general use in cabinet work in wet tropical areas where high humidities prevail during the summer months. While high moisture resistant fibreboards can be used in these applications particleboard usually provides a more economical option. However, if the situation is such that the board is continually exposed to moisture conditions where the moisture content is above 20% it will then be subject to decay and a preservative treated product will be required.

Where particleboard is being cut into various widths for shelving usually timber is fixed to the long edges and this considerably improves the bending strength. Tables giving the load capacities are available for the different shelving products produced.

As with plywood, particleboard is subject to decay if the moisture content remains above 20%. Again, also the term exterior grade particleboard only guarantees freedom from breakdown of the board due to moisture contamination not resistance to decay. Particleboard flooring which does have to be exposed for a period can contain extra waterproofing agents such as waxes. Wet area flooring for use under shower trays, baths and tiles in wet areas contains a fungicide to inhibit decay.

Fibreboard

Fibreboard is a further development of particleboard. Instead of the chips being coated with glue and pressed into a sheet the chips are converted into wood fibres by thermomechanical refining. In this process wood chips are 'cooked' and then rubbed apart into fibre bundles. As the fibres are all basically of the same size, they need no screening. These fibres are mthen mixed with the resin binder, normally urea formaldehyde, formed into a matt and hot pressed to produce a sheet. Fine sanding and sawing to size then follows. The result is a sheet with very uniform characteristics and because timber fibres are minute it is not possible to see the fibres with the naked eye. In this it is very different from particleboard where the individual chips are clearly visible. This very fine surface appearance allows fibreboard to be given a paint coating on both the faces and edges and produce a high-quality finish comparable to solid timber. This is particularly useful in cabinet work. While particleboard is nomally produced with a fine finish on the faces of the board the edges show the larger particles. This then requires covering the edges with timber, veneer or similar products to obtain a fine finish like fibreboard.

Board sizes vary according to the individual plant and sizes up to 3600mm x 1200mm are produced but the regular size is 2400mm x 1200mm. Medium density Fibreboard [MDF] is the regular board available but a denser high-density board HDF is manufactured and this product finds particular application as the substrate in prefinished flooring where its hardness gives extra resistance to indentation.

As with particleboard both interior and high moisture resistant [HMR] adhesives can be used in its manufacture. HMR fibreboard is the preferred type to be used for cabinet work in areas where moisture can be a problem such as bathrooms and kitchens. It is also the preferred recommendation in furniture and cabinet work in high humidity tropical areas.

Fibreboard, in common with other boards such as particleboard, will expand with increases in atmospheric moisture. Interior fibreboard, once wet, will not return to the original size after drying and in this is similar to particleboard and not like timber.

Hardboard

Hardboard is another sheet material that is manufactured from wood. It differs from other timber-based sheet material in that no synthetic resins are used in its manufacture. The agent bonding the fibre particles together is the lignin naturally occurring in the timber. The only added product is a very small percentage of petroleum-based waxes which give it extra resistance to water. Where plywood, particleboard and fibreboard mostly use softwoods such as radiata pine as their timber component, hardboards use hardwood from Australia's eucalypt forests. The most common species used are blackbutt, spotted gum, ironbarks and stringybarks. They are drawn from sustainably managed forests and hardwood plantations around Australia's only manufacturing facility at Raymond Terrace near Newcastle New South Wales. The product is sold under the name Weathertex.

The process involves debarking and then chipping the logs. The chips are then put through a process using steam and high pressure to 'explode' the chips into their component fibres. In the process starch and sugars are removed. The resulting product is then mixed with wax and then formed into a matt. This matt is then by the use of hot platens compressed into a sheet and in this process the lignin is reactivated and bonds the sheet together. The board resulting is then dried to 8% moisture content and machined to 9.5mm thickness. The sheets may then have the surface machined to give a rough finish [e.g ruff sawn,] or given a coat of acrylic primer for pre-primed boards and either cut into various sized sheets or sawn into the various sizes of weatherboards.

The product range produced is quite large with a range of sheets for external and internal use sized from 3660mm long down to 915mm long and 1220mm to 1196mm wide.

Weatherboards in different profiles range down from 3660mm long and come in a number of widths from 300mm down. Methods of fixing and the product range is normally available from supplying merchants.

Hardboard is produced to meet the relevant Australian Standard AS/NZS1859.4. Like all timber products it comes into equilibrium with the surrounding atmosphere and in so doing expands or contracts. However, again like all processed boards this movement is far less than solid timber. In the case of hardboard, across the moisture range of 8% to 18% a total increase or decrease in dimension of 0.25% will occur. For example, across the 1200mm width of a board an increase of 3mm would occur if the moisture content increased from 8% to 18% [solid hardwood boards aggregating 1200mm would expand approximately 45mm].

The Australian eucalypt hardwoods used in manufacture are high in durability and as starch and sugars are removed in the manufacturing process, it has good resistance to decay [fungal attack] and could be assessed as Class 2 or better and be suitable for external out of ground use.

Bamboo Composite Board

Because there is a relative abundance of bamboo forests and it is quick growing, bamboo has become quite popular as a raw material in producing composite boards. Although the bamboos are not classified as trees, they like other members of the plant kingdom share much in common with trees. As mentioned previously in the chapter on the structure of timber one of the essential compounds that makes up the cell structure is cellulose and this also applies to bamboo. As this can then be sourced from bamboo the development of bamboo products such as clothing as an alternative to cotton which is also cellulose is obvious. The essential difference from timber is the growth habit and absence of a solid trunk.

In the production of composite board, the bamboo is harvested after 4 to 5 years as the source material. The plant is left to sucker and again produce more shoots which are again harvested once the correct size is attained. There are a large number of species available and only some are found suitable for the production of a composite board. Similarly, only some species have shoots that are edible for human consumption and others suitable as food for pandas.

Briefly the manufacturing process involves the following steps:

- The bamboo stalks are cut to the length required
- It is split and sized and internodal knots removed
- After hot washing to remove contaminants, it is kiln dried
- [The strips are assembled into boards of the size required, glued and hot pressed
- The boards are then sized and sanded
- The glues used are selected for low formaldehyde emission. The finished product has a density around 1000 kg per m3 and a relatively high Janka hardness of around 15 kilo newtons making it harder than most hardwood timbers.

The product finds many uses ranging from furniture and cabinet ware to tongue and grooved flooring. In these applications changes in dimension with changes in atmospheric moisture content are small because the substantial amount of resin present. The resin itself is not affected by changes in moisture content. However, if continually exposed to higher moisture levels the product tends to blacken and slowly decay. In addition to the common uses listed above a wide range of small articles are processed using bamboo board as the source material.

Chapter 10: Glue Laminated Timber Products

This chapter covers products manufactured by glue laminating solid timber or veneers to give a range of seasoned larger section timber products. The processes use different glues according to the specific uses intended. The product range differs from those covered in chapter 9 above in that the products are greater in thickness and are more closely aligned to normal solid timber sizes. However, they fill a need for seasoned large section members not possible to be produced in normal timber mill production. The range of products included in this chapter is as follows:

- Laminated Veneer Lumber [LVL]
- Glue Laminated Timber [Glulam]
- Cross Laminated Timber [CLT]
- Finger jointed Timber

Laminated Veneer Lumber [LVL]

LVL, as it normally referred to, is an extremely versatile and useful product now widely used in many structural applications particularly house construction. For larger size beams it provides a seasoned product whereas in the case of solid timber the only option is to use unseasoned timber. The other option would be to use laminated timber beams but the product is more costly. The detail involved in production is outlined below. In brief it involves using sheets of veneer that are glued together and the sheets then sawn into widths to give the desired depth required. The desired thickness of the member is achieved by the number of sheets of veneer glued. By scarf jointing of the ends of the sheets of veneer long lengths can be produced. Some plants only scarf joint the outer veneers and butt joint the inner. There is no real limit to the lengths which are only governed by space in the plant and practical transport limitations.

Manufacture

The production of the veneer uses the same techniques as in plywood manufacture viz. rotary peeling of billets of timber. In Australia most commonly radiata pine is the preferred timber for availability and cost reasons. The rotary peeled veneer sheets are normally 3mm thick. Veneers are then dried before the next step in the process.

With normal plywood layup, the long bands are progressively laid on the cross bands with both veneers having the tight side up. The

LVL Beams

normal flat cross laminated plywood sheet results so long as correct procedures are followed. The layup of LVL is different. Instead of the grain direction of each sheet of veneer being alternately at right angles to the next sheet [cross laminated], the grain of each sheet of veneer is in the same direction. However, there is an inherent problem in that when rotary peeling a veneer from a round log there is a natural tendency for curvature to occur and in flattening the veneer the side nearest the knife is compressed and becomes the tight side and on the other side this opens up the texture and gives the 'loose' side. To prevent this curvature that would happen in the LVL layup procedure a special procedure is involved which prevents the problem happening. The veneers are laid up with a tight side to a tight side then a loose side to a loose side. However, the outer faces have the tight side facing out. Glue is applied to one side of each veneer and the scarf jointed sheets in the lay up progressively fed into the hot press to give the final length required. The number of sheets of veneer being glued is governed by the thickness required for the final product. After cooling the sheets are then gang sawed to give the required depth of the LVL.

Product Use

The veneers can be pretreated to give decay and termite resistance if necessary. LVL has superior strength requirements to conventional timber due to the use of veneers.

Tables are available from the manufacturers' web sites giving span tables covering size requirements for the different situations. If used in external situations preservative treatment to give addition to decay resistance is required. Also, in these situations normal protection with finishes is required. The photo shows a typical application where LVL beams have been used to support a roof structure. By carefully looking at the bottom edge of the photo the veneers can be seen.

Glue Laminated Timber [Glulam]

The concept of gluing smaller thickness seasoned timber together to give deeper section members has been practiced for a long time. The process overcomes the problem that large section timber in the seasoned state is not available in the normal mill operations. If unseasoned timber is used it can create problems with shrinkage in most applications. For example, a 200mm x 50mm unseasoned hardwood beam can shrink by up to 12mm in depth as it eventually dries out. Both seasoned pine and seasoned hardwood are regularly used in laminating into larger sections.

Manufacture

- The seasoned laminates are assembled. Moisture content is usually 12%.
- The laminates are then finger-jointed if necessary to give the desired laminate lengths for the beam being manufactured.
- The laminates are then assembled and hot pressed using a structural glue.
- The beam is removed, cooled and dressed to the exact size nominated.

The thickness of the laminates varies according to the plant but is frequently 30mm and widths can range up from 70mm according to the size required. With the wide range of laminate sizes available a great range of finished beam sizes is possible. However, because span tables have to be produced for users to secure beam sizes for different spans, constraints are necessary in the size of laminates used. However specially sized beams can be engineered for special applications. Long lengths are available, in some plants up to 18 metres or more and curved beams can be produced for special orders. Hardwood which is more difficult to glue relies on resorcinol glue whereas polyurethane glues are suitable for pine. However, both are long life structural glues.

Species Used

This is dependent on the plant location and what are the local species. In Victoria it could be messmate and radiata pine, in Queensland spotted gum and plantation pine from local forests. It is necessary to check with the supplier in the region as to what is available.

Standards

All beams are manufactured in accordance with the procedures laid down by the Glue Laminated Timber Association of Australia.

Design Tables

The various manufacturers produce design tables which can then be used to select the correct size for each individual application.

Typical Applications

Glulam is still widely used in all types of construction where a long length seasoned member is required as for example as lintels, bearers, beams over garage doors and in special designs [LVL also has a place in this market]. The aesthetic appearance of selected species is favoured for use in post and beam construction where the beams are featured in the exposed roof structures. Where used in situations exposed to the weather or termite attack precautions have to be taken. Non-durable species such as pine have to be preservative treated. If durable hardwoods are used the outer surfaces need protection against weathering with a good paint system. The following photograph shows the use of decorative hardwood beams in the roof structure at the National Arboretum in Canberra.

The laminated beams have been used in the form of curved beams and also for the straight supporting members.

Laminated Beams, Canberra Arboretum

Cross Laminated Timber [CLT]

Cross laminated timber, or CLT as it is commonly known, is a relatively new product in Australia but has been used in many countries for a number of years. The product was first used in Switzerland in the 1970s. The particular application has been in the construction of medium rise buildings particularly in Canada and the USA and some countries in Europe.

In its structure, CLT consists of several layers of kiln dried laminates laid in alternating directions, bonded with structural glues and pressed to form a solid rectangular panel. CLT panels consist of an odd number of layers [3 to 7] and if required can be sanded. In Australia, 35mm thick radiata pine is the preferred timber used because of ready availability, favourable cost and ease of gluing. At the manufacturing plant, once the panels are produced, they are then cut to the sizes required for the structure and if desired the necessary door and window openings can be cut into the panels using CNC [Computer Numerical Control] routers. The final result is an extremely strong, very stiff and stable product ready for delivery to site.

As can be well understood, the design of each panel is dependent on skilled timber engineering matching the panels produced to the engineering requirements of the overall structure to be built. Where panels are used in exterior situations the radiata pine is preservative treated to protect it against possible decay. This also gives protection against termites if these are a hazard at the location.

CLT as it comes in prefabricated panels ready for assembly means much faster assembly and construction without the need for concrete slab floors or steel and masonry walls. It is also lighter in weight and has better thermal efficiency. Around the world it is being incorporated into the various building codes. It also locks away a great amount of carbon permanently in the timber used.

Initially the product was used mainly in medium rise buildings up to 10 stories but wider applications are being found such as floors in high set housing. As time proceeds further applications are sure to be developed because of its special properties. The illustration shows a medium rise building built using cross laminated timber.

Medium-rise Building using CLT

Finger Jointed Timber

The previous sections on glue laminating have covered the various products that can be manufactured by taking smaller section timber and building them to give larger section timber. This covers the conventional laminated beam and the newer application of cross laminating to give cross laminated timber. In the process, glue is applied to the faces of the timber being glued. Finger jointing is a different process in that the pieces are joined at their ends to give longer lengths but it is necessary to machine fingers and corresponding slots to the ends of the boards to give the joint structural strength. Glue is applied to the fingers and the pieces clamped together. While finger jointing has long been one of a number of methods of joining timber such as mortice and tenon and tongue and groove, it was never easy to accurately cut fingers and the corresponding slots into the ends of pieces of timber. Finger jointing is a very important process as it is a means of utilizing short lengths of timber which would otherwise be wasted. It is also a means of obtaining longer lengths of timber that normally would not be available from normal production.

However, over time. as the development of wood working machines proceeded and became more sophisticated with computer control, high precision finger jointing to produce longer lengths of timber has become commonplace. However, it does involve a reasonable scale of production to justify the cost of the machines required. There is a considerable range of manufacturers of wood working machinery particularly in Europe and America. This machinery is available in a range of options from simpler manual to semi-automatic to highly sophisticated fully automatic computer-controlled machines. In amongst this range are machines devoted to finger jointing.

With a range of manufacturers each with their own range of machines there is obviously a wide range of thicknesses, widths and lengths of laminates that can be handled. For example, one well known manufacturer can cover thicknesses from 16mm to 80mm, widths from 18mm to 200mm and laminate lengths from 150mm to 1m [some machines can handle 2m and 3m lengths]. Most machines are high speed operations. Some for example can carry out 180 joints per minute. It is also easy to understand with the foregoing ranges in dimensions that no one machine can handle this very wide range of options and each machine has its own limits. Therefore, any organization wishing to go into finger jointing of timber needs to work closely with potential machinery suppliers to select the right machine for their needs. The other option is to locate a business already set up for finger jointing and use their services.

In the operation of the machines, in simple terms the laminates to be finger jointed are fed to the machine, the fingers and slots are cut in the adjoining laminates, the specified glue is spread on the fingers and the machine then clamps the fingers into the slots. The joined piece of timber feeds out of the machine along the production line where any sideways movement is minimized until the glue cures.

While end jointing is the predominant application there has been some move into vertical finger jointing where thicknesses are increased by cutting by fingers and slots cut into adjoining faces.

There are several situations where end jointing finds application. Two of the most common are as follows.

- Joining of short lengths of timber. The source of the short lengths can arise from two sources. Firstly, as a result of normal timber milling operations and secondly as a result of upgrading the quality of the timber by docking out defects such as knots etc., to produce a select piece of timber. Modern machines are capable of handling infeed lengths down to 150mm. Most machines can produce lengths up to 6m.
- Producing laminates for the production of laminated beams
- Where longer length laminates are required in the production of laminated beams where longer length beams are often the norm, finger jointing of either the hardwood or softwood laminates is frequently used. In this operation long life structural glues in bonding the finger joints are of course necessary.

Finger jointing has thus become a very important operation in the production of a large range of timber products and has offset the problems that used happen in trying to source quantities of longer length timber.

Finger jointed timber

Chapter 11: How Problems in the Use of Timber Can Occur – Case Studies

As mentioned in the Introduction, problems occur in all types of construction regardless of the products being used through either lack of essential knowledge of the products being used or failure to use this knowledge either intentionally or unintentionally and this also occurs with timber. The purpose of this chapter is to give readers the opportunity to read about actual cases where timber problems occurred due to those involved not having a thorough understanding of timber and the very many properties to be considered in its use. There are some very interesting cases. The chapter also covers situations where recommended procedures were not followed. To correctly use many of these procedures usually first of all requires a good understanding of timber and its various properties.

By studying the various cases it is hoped that it will make the readers more familiar with the importance of various applicable sections in the *Essential Guide*. Also, by reading where some users and designers ran into trouble it will help others avoid similar situations. Unlike other building products, timber is a renewable resource so it is important that its use be maximized but this depends on ensuring that in all applications the final result meets expectations.

Each of the twelve cases taken will be examined giving details of the situation. In some of the examples it was possible to secure photos of the end result which illustrate the situation better. The cases used are just a few taken from the author's hundreds of site inspections over more than twenty years.

In examining the cases, readers will probably notice there are some common causes:

- Not using timber at the right moisture content for the application.
- Decay due to use of timber with insufficient durability for the situation.
- Using untreated sapwood in exterior situations.
- Selection of the incorrect timber for the use.
- Not following recommended procedures correctly.

It is sincerely hoped the cases will prove interesting reading and assist in illustrating the great amount of information that is present in the *Essential Guide*.

Case 1: Problem Decay of decking timber in a fully exposed deck.

Cause. The use of decking timber containing untreated sapwood

This case was one involving the use of spotted gum boards for decking. This species is popular and highly recommended for this use. However, as the sapwood of hardwoods is not durable in external situations the decking timber supplied must be either free of sapwood or any sapwood present must be preservative treated. The site details were that the deck was fully exposed and within 2 to 3 years the residents could put a foot through many of the boards resulting in a severe safety hazard. An off cut of the decking timber which the owner had kept was found to contain an untreated sapwood band surrounding the sound internal truewood. Many of the boards were obviously mostly sapwood as the whole board had decayed. The decay of the boards can be seen in the first photograph. The readers should also quickly identify that the cause of the problem was untreated sapwood being used in an external situation. Why sapwood has minimal durability and truewood can have very high durability is

explained in detail in Chapter 7. The problem was found in two other decks but there could have been more in other areas. How the decking was produced without somebody noticing that the sapwood had not been preservative treated could not be ascertained. Remedial action involved replacement of all the faulty boards which comprised a large proportion of the deck. The photo below shows the lighter coloured sapwood surrounding the truewood; the first shows the decay in the deck. This decay can be seen in the yellowish patches occurring across the deck.

Decay in a Deck

Untreated Sapwood in Decking Timber

Case 2: Problem – Lifting of floor boards in North Queensland

Cause. Insufficient knowledge of importance of correct moisture content and also necessary expansion joints when laying floors

This case involved the lifting of 80mm floor boards in a very attractive solid hardwood strip floor in tropical North Queensland. The owners were very unhappy and the builder who laid the floor was not sure as to why the floor had lifted. The floor had been laid in November and during heavy rain in January the floor lifted.

Inspection of the floor in early March showed the average board widths were 80.6mm [up by 0.6mm] and the moisture content was 14%. Using unit movement calculations [which are explained in Chapter 6] it can be calculated that the 0.6mm increase in width approximately equates to a 2% increase in moisture. As the floor was tested at 14% moisture this indicates the floor was laid at 12% moisture content. A moisture content of at least 13% or a little higher plus very adequate expansion joints is needed in the wet tropical regions. During the winter months flooring moisture contents are typically around 13% but in periods of heavy rainfall in summer flooring moisture contents can rise to 17% or more.

Inspection of what expansion joints had been provided showed only two 10mm gaps at the walls and no intermediate expansion gaps. These gaps are very essential particularly in tropical areas. With runs of six metres across the width [75 boards] and a board expansion well in excess of 6mm and limited expansion allowance it is clear the floor had expanded against the side walls. It then had to lift. The reason for the problem was a lack of understanding of equilibrium moisture content [EMC] and its effect when laying floors plus not following recommended procedures as set down by the Australian Timber Flooring Association. Preferably it is wise to engage a professional floor layer thoroughly familiar with the correct procedures for the area and who is equipped with a moisture meter to check moisture levels in the timber supplied. If none are available the other option is to very thoroughly follow recommended procedures not just nail down the flooring as supplied. Remedial action involved refixing the floor and installing adequate intermediate expansion joints. The onsite photo shows the lifting of the boards that occurred. The fact that many floors are laid successfully without checking moisture content of the flooring supplied happens because by chance all of the factors involved particularly moisture content happen to be correct. The photo shows the lifted boards.

Lifting of Floorboards, Townsville

Case 3: Problem – Severe decay of external treated pine posts

Cause. Timber not adequately treated to Australian standards

An inspection of an entry deck and flight of stairs to a high set house revealed extreme decay of the pine posts and other supporting pine members. The pine had been purchased as being preservative treated. The decay was so severe that the whole structure was in danger of collapsing and unsafe to use. The builder's supplier in good faith had purchased the product from overseas as fully treated pine which it clearly was not. There was no branding on the timber to indicate the treatment level or the treatment plant. Reference to the preservation section in the *Essential Guide* in Chapter 7 sets out the different treatment levels for different situations and clearly explains the branding required to be stamped on the timber. In this situation preservation treatment to H3 level as set out in *AS/NZS 1604.1* is necessary. The whole structure needed rebuilding using pine treated to H3 level from Australian suppliers. The photo shows that the decay was so severe that a screwdriver could be easily pushed through the posts.

Decay of Supporting Pine Posts

Case 4: Problem – Unsatisfactory appearance of timber used in a feature ceiling

Cause. Use of unseasoned timber in an internal joinery situation

Inspection showed the very unsatisfactory appearance of hoop pine used in an office complex as can be seen from the photo below. Where the pieces of timber met twisting and warping had affected the straightness of each line of the feature boards. The concept of using a feature timber ceiling fitted in nicely with recent research that has shown that the use of timber in office and other internal situations greatly improves well-being and productivity. In this case instead of using seasoned pine, for some reason unseasoned timber had been used and in drying out to come into equilibrium with the atmospheric moisture conditions in the offices twisting and warping of many of the boards occurred. Why unseasoned timber was used could not be ascertained. Prevention of this and similar kinds of problems such as shrinkage after installation requires that only seasoned timber be used in internal joinery applications. Remedial action involved waiting until all the boards had fully seasoned and then replacing the twisted ones with seasoned timber. Chapter 6 has a wealth of information about timber and moisture.

The photo clearly shows how the timber had twisted and warped leading to an unsatisfactory appearance.

Ceiling Timbers

Case 5: Problem – Severe decay in treated pine used to build pergolas

Cause. Failure to follow procedures when pine having surface treatment only is used

The pergolas were found on inspection to have decayed severely leading to the poor appearance and possibility of collapse in unfavourable climatic conditions. Some treated pine available on the market does not give complete penetration of preservative through the whole of the timber only surface treatment. Reference to the Preservation Section in Chapter 7 of the *Essential Guide* explains this in detail. Where this type of treated timber is used it requires further regular treatment of any sawcuts, notching, drilling, planing or heavy sanding with a paint on preservative such as copper naphthenate. As decay occurred it would appear this procedure was not carried out, hence the problems. This problem with failure to use further treatment is not uncommon even though it is normal for the relevant instructions to come with the timber. It is helpful if those using the timber are advised of just what timber is supplied along with any special requirements covering its use.

The photo shows the severe decay that occurred around the joints where sawcuts and notching were necessary in the construction. The presence of severe decay is illustrated by the fact that a screwdriver could be pushed right into the pine as shown in the photo.

Decay of Treated Pine in Pergolas

Case 6: Problem – Decay of structural grade waterproof pine plywood in external application

Cause. Failure to understand that 'waterproof' plywood does not mean it will not decay in external situations exposed to rain but only means it will not delaminate

In this case structural waterproof exterior grade pine plywood was used to lift the height of a previously constructed concrete block fence to give better privacy from the street for the residents. It was decided that an economic, quick and easy solution would be to mount a 400mm high strip of 18mm structural grade exterior plywood on top of the blocks instead of having to lay more courses of bricks. In a relatively short space of time the plywood began to decay and the structure became loose as the fixings holding the plywood in place became ineffective. The decay also affected the bond between the veneers resulting in delamination. Where exterior grade pine structural plywood is being used in fully exposed exterior permanent situations the veneers need to be preservative treated to H3 level. The same situation exists with marine grade plywood. The term exterior plywood only relates to the ability of the glue bond to resist delamination in the presence of water and does not cover resistance to decay. This is all explained in detail in the plywood section of Chapter 9 of the *Essential Guide*.

The photo shows the decay of the plywood which has then affected the glue bond.

Decay of External Pine Plywood

Case 7. Problem – Severe lifting of timber floor

Cause. Failure to follow recommended procedures particularly in relation to sub floor requirements

This case involved a nice country home built 600mm off the ground. Construction had involved putting down a plywood subfloor on the bearers and joists and building the wall and roof structure using this as a working platform. A very attractive hardwood strip floor was then fixed to the plywood. The under-floor area was enclosed on two sides with a concrete block wall and fully open on the other two sides. The surrounding garden area was above the level of the under-floor area and in addition was not sloped away from the house perimeter. As a result, in the first rain storm the underneath of the house was flooded with water due primarily to surface water flowing in from the outside area. The under-floor area was always damp, vegetation was prolific and eventually the timber floor as it lifted in moisture content lifted off the plywood in many places and became very 'drummy.' On inspection the block wall surrounding two sides was also found to have only a few very small vent holes. The result was that there was no cross ventilation of the underfloor area to sweep away moisture rising from the ground even if drainage in from the outside had not occurred. Failure to follow the correct procedures which involves good subfloor ventilation and having a slope of the surrounding away from the perimeter was the prime cause of the problem.

Remedial action involved landscaping around the perimeter of the house to give a positive slope away and prevent water coming in plus installing vents meeting the requirements of NCC BCA in the masonry walls on the two sides that were closed in. Remedial action also involved waiting until the floor moisture had come down to correct levels in line with the prevailing atmospheric levels and then refixing the floor boards. The photo shows the underfloor area and the abundance of vegetation.

Subfloor Problem Causing Floor to Lift

Case 8: Problem – Large gaps between boards in feature timber floor

Cause. Laying the floor at the incorrect moisture content

In this case the appearance of an attractive hardwood timber floor was being marred by large gaps between boards. The builder attempted to fill them but as the timber shrinks and expands with changes in atmospheric moisture the filling fell out. The builder could not understand why the problem had occurred. Standard laying procedures require that flooring be laid at a moisture content that is recommended for the particular geographic area and that the moisture content of the flooring be checked with a moisture meter to make sure it complies. Based on the median annual EMC [equilibrium moisture content] for the area this moisture content should have been in the 11% to 12% range. Measurement of the board widths and using unit shrinkage data for the species involved revealed that many boards were supplied at the higher limit of the flooring moisture content standard viz. 14%. In this case the builder had just taken the packs of flooring as delivered, assumed they were right to lay and laid them without checking the moisture content. Trying to fill gaps is rarely successful due to the boards expanding and contracting with changes in atmospheric moisture. Much of the flooring had to be lifted and relaid to overcome the problem.

The photo shows the gaps between the boards.

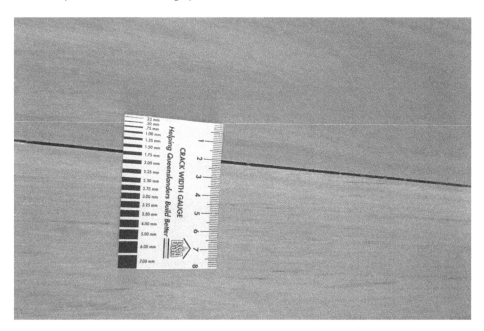

Gap in Internal Floor Boards

Case 9: Problem – Decay of hardwood beams and joists under a deck

Cause. Use of a hardwood timber species that was not rated as Class 2 durability which is recommended for this application

In this case, five years after construction, the supporting beams and joists under a deck that was largely exposed to any rain were found to be decayed resulting in many of the decking boards becoming loose. The result was possible collapse of a section of the deck plus an ever-present trip hazard from boards that had become loose because of the decay of the underlying timber. When the builder was called in, he could not explain to the owners why the decay had occurred. His reasoning was that as he had purchased F17 hardwood timber it should not decay. On inspection it was found that the species purchased was a hardwood species which, although it could be graded to meet F17 strength requirements, only met durability Class 3. For external applications above ground where hardwood timbers are used recommended minimum durability for supporting timbers under exposed decks is Class 2. A full explanation of durability classes is explained in Chapter 7 of the *Essential Guide* including data on many common timbers. It is not uncommon for many builders to be unaware that there are a number of structural hardwoods that are rated as Class 3 on the durability scale. Remedial work was quite extensive as all the deck not completely under cover had to be rebuilt. Unfortunately, no clear photo could be secured showing the decay.

Case 10: Problem – Failure of deck built very close to the ground

Cause. Recommended procedures for this application were not followed

This case involved a deck built next to an inground swimming pool. When inspected the deck timbers as a whole had partly lifted off the joists and were jammed so close together that, to be separated, they had to be cut out with a saw. Inspection underneath revealed the joists were supported on stirrups set in concrete pads. The area under the deck was a pool of water. Moisture content of the decking boards was close to 30%. There was no air flow through under the deck and the under-deck area had no slope to allow any water accumulating to drain away.

Obviously, the recommended procedures in building decks close to ground had clearly not been followed. This requires good cross flow ventilation under the deck, drainage away of water from pool splashing or during times of rainfall and use of drainage pipes if the topography is not suitable. Also necessary is extra gapping between boards [90mm = 5mm], ensuring all timbers used are termite-proof and supporting timbers rated durability Class 1 above ground. It is essential standard procedures be followed and clearly in this case this had not happened. Remedial action was extensive.

The site situation was such that a clear photo showing the causes of the problem could not be secured.

Case 11: Problem – Decay of laminated pine beam used in an external situation

Cause. Failure to realize that preservative treatment was necessary

This case involved a number of small country cottages that were let out to tourists. The rooms of the cottage led out to a covered deck where two untreated laminated pine beams on the sides of the decks had been used as perimeter beams. Hardwood joists in between the beams and parallel to the house were supported on joist hangers on the beams. The decking was nailed to the joists and also directly to the top of the beams. Severe decay occurred to the external laminated beams under the decking resulting in the decking boards fixed to the perimeter beams lifting, the external rail structure above the beams collapsing and the integrity of the hardwood joists fixed to the beams being severely compromised. Being on the perimeter, the beams were subject to rain and damp conditions. A dangerous situation for tourists therefore occurred. The original design called for durable hardwood laminated beams but pine laminated beams were substituted to save cost. Unfortunately, the requirement that laminated pine beams used in exterior situations have to be preservative treated to the correct level must have been overlooked. As a number of decks were involved remedial costs were appreciable. Reference to Chapter 7 before construction on durability particularly as it applies to untreated pine would have alerted the builder and owner to the potential problem. Steps could have then been taken to preservative-treat the substituted pine laminated beams to H3 level.

Decay of Laminated Beam

162

Case 12: Problem – Timber decking bought at auction was faulty.

Cause. Product was not checked for quality before purchase by a qualified timber person

This is not the usual type of timber problem but has been included to illustrate that extreme care needs to be taken if buying timber at auction. Sometimes sellers can be sending quality timber to auction because of a need to reduce stock or because of cessation of business. At other times, problems may have occurred during manufacture and auction is a means of quitting faulty stock. In all cases the buyer should seek the services of a qualified timber person to carefully check the quality before purchase.

In this case, because the owner wanted a very large deck, an effort was made to save costs by buying at auction. Inspection of the deck after it had been built revealed the boards had been badly machined with variations in thickness between boards of up to 3mm and variations in thickness along individual boards of 3mm. Sadly, the carpenter tried to lay the whole deck and compensate along the boards for different thicknesses along the boards by using loose nails as wedges. This was clearly an impossible task as along individual boards thickness varied from 77mm to 80mm. The net result was that the boards were not firmly fixed and frequently there were 3mm differences in thicknesses where boards butted. This then caused a dangerous trip hazard. It was never ascertained what if any remedial action was taken. Why the carpenter continued to lay the decking once he discovered the problem also could not be ascertained. As mentioned above, if costs of timber are to be saved for any project by buying at auction, the aid of a very qualified timber person should be secured to inspect the timber before putting in a bid.

It was not possible to obtain a clear photo that showed the faults in the timber.

Appendices

The purpose of including an appendix is to provide as a quick ready reference to twelve of the more common properties of some 38 species of timbers in common use in Australia. Two appendices are provided. Appendix 1 covers 23 of the more common eucalypt species, and Appendix 2 covers six common Australian softwoods and a selection of nine imported species which includes hardwoods and softwoods. Each appendix is split into two groups A and B. Group A covers the botanical names plus the following properties strength group, joint group and density. Group B covers shrinkage, durability hardness and lyctus susceptibility. In the case of hardwoods, as the commonly used name used around Australia does not always relate to the same species, the inclusion of the botanical name then identifies the species.

The purpose of splitting the properties up into groups A and B is to enable the information to fit on the page of a normal sized book.

Appendix 1

Group A

Name	Botanical Name	Strength Group Unseas	Seas	Joint Unseas	Group Seas	Density Unseas	Seas
Ash Alpine	e.*delegatensis*	S4	SD4	J3	JD3	1050	650
Ash Mountain	e.*regnans*	S4	SD3	J3	JD3	1050	650
Blackbutt	e.*pilularis*	S2	SD2	J2	JD2	1150	900
Blackbutt New England	e.*andrusii*	S3	SD3	J2	JD2	1150	850
Bloodwood red	*corymbia gummifera*	S3	SD3	J1	JD1	1300	1010
Box Brush	*Lophostoman Confertus*	S3	SD3	J2	JD2	1100	900
Box Grey	e.*microcarpa*	S1	SD1	J1	JD1	1200	1100
Gum flooded	e.*grandis*	S3	SD3	J2	JD2	1100	750
Gum forest red	e.*tereticornis*	S3	SD4	J1	JD1	1150	1000
Gum grey	e.*propinqua*	S1	SD2	J1	JD1	1240	1080
Gum manna	e.*viminalis*	S4	SD4	J3	JD2	1100	800
Gum river red	e.*camaldulensis*	S5	SD5	J2	JD2	1150	900
Gum spotted	*corymbia Maculata*	S2	SD2	J1	JD1	1200	1100
Gum Sydney blue	e.*saligna*	S3	SD3	J2	JD2	1100	850
Ironbark grey	e.*paniculata*	S1	SD1	J1	JD1	1200	1100
Ironbark reds	e.*creba* e.*sideroxylon*	S2	SD3	J1	JD1	1200	1100
Jarrah	e.*marginata*	S4	SD4	J2	JD2	1100	800
Karri	e.*diversicolor*	S3	SD2	J2	JD2	1150	900
Messmate	e.*obliqua*	S3	SD3	J3	JD3	1100	750

Group A (continued)

Name	Botanical Name	Strength Group Unseas	Seas	Joint Group Unseas	Seas	Density Unseas	Seas
Stringybark	*e.laevopinea*	S3	SD3	J2	JD2	1150	900
Tallowwood	*e.microcorys*	S2	SD2	J1	JD2	1200	1000
Turpentine	*Syncarpia glomulifera*	S3	SD3	J2	JD2	1050	950

NOTES:

- Density is quoted in kg/m3
- There are two varieties of red ironbark, narrow leaf and broad leaf both with similar properties. Only the narrow leaf variety is listed.
- Spotted gum in Queensland is also known as *e.citriodora*
- Tasmanian Oak is a variable mix of alpine and mountain ash with messmate. The data can therefore be a mix of the three species.
- The stringybark listed is also called silvertop stringbark. There are also white and yellow varieties with similar properties.
- Flooded gum is also commonly called rose gum.

Group B

Name	Shrinkage % Tang Unit	Durability above ground	Class in ground	Hardness Seas Janka	Affect of Lyctus borer
Ash alpine	8.5 0.35	3	4	5	S
Ash mountain	13.3 0.36	3	4	5	NS
Blackbutt	7.3 0.37	1	2	8.9	NS
Blackbutt New England	8.5 0.36	1	2	9.2	S
Bloodwood red	4.0 ---	1	1	VH	S
Box brush	9.7 0.38	3	3	9.1	NS
Box grey	8.2 0.42	1	1	13.0	S
Gum flooded	7.5 0.39	2	3	7.3	NS
Gum forest Red	8.6 0.34	1	1	11.3	NS
Gum grey	7.0 ---	1	1	14.0	S
Gum river red	8.9 0.31	1	2	9.7	S
Gum spotted	6.1 0.38	1	2	10.1	S
Gum Sydney Blue	9.5 0.35	2	3	9.0	S
Ironbark grey	7.5 0.39	1	1	16.3	S
Ironbark reds	6.3 0.37	1	1	11.9	S
Jarrah	7.4 0.30	2	2	8.5	NS
Karri	9.9 0.40	2	3	9.0	NS
Messmate	11.3 0.36	3	3	7.4	S
Stringybark	7.5 0.37	2	3	8.6	NS
Tallowwood	6.0 0.37	1	1	8.6	S
Turpentine	13.0 0.35	1	1	11.6	NS

NOTES:

- S means susceptible and NS means not susceptible to lyctus
- VH means very hard – no Janka data was available
- Janka hardness has only been quoted on seasoned timbers as in uses such as flooring this information is important.
- The durability class relates to the heartwood only. Any sapwood present is class 4 durability.

Appendix 2

This appendix covers the properties of Australia's more common softwoods and also a range of imported softwoods and hardwoods. As in the case of Australian hardwoods in Appendix 1, in Appendix 2 the information is also split into two groups to enable it to fit on to the page of a normal book.

Group A

Name	Botanical Name	Strength Unseas	Group Seas	Joint Unseas	Group Seas	Density Unseas	Seas
Pine caribbean	*pinus caribaea*	S6	SD6	J4	JD9	---	545
Pine Celery top	*phyllodadus asplenifolius*	S4	SD5	J3	JD3	1050	650
Pine White Cypress	*callitris columellaris*	S5	SD6	J3	JD3	850	700
Pine hoop	*araucaria cunninghami*	S6	SD5	J4	JD4	800	550
Pine radiata	*pinus radiata*	S6	SD6	J4	JD4	800	550
Pine slash	*pinus elliotii*	S5	SD5	J3	JD3	850	650
IMPORTED TIMBERS							
Calantas	*toona calantas*	S6	SD7	---	JD4	---	500
Balau	*shorea species*	S2	SD3	J2	JD2	1150	900
Durian	*durio species*	S4	SD4	---	JD4		
Kapur	*dryobalops spp*	S3	SD3	J2	JD2	1100	750
Meranti light red	*shorea species*	---	SD7	---	JD5	---	400
Merbau [Kwila]	*intsia bijuga*	S2	SD3	J2	JD2	1150	850
Oregon	*pseudotsuga menziesii*	S5	SD5	J4	JD4	710	550
Teak	*tectona grandis*	S6	SD6	J2	JD2	---	670
Western red cedar	*thuja plicata*	S7	SD8	---	JD6	---	380

NOTES:

- spp is abbreviation for species
- Calantas is similar in colour and properties to Nth Qld red cedar

- Only three plantation pines are quoted viz. Caribbean, Radiata and Slash. Other varieties are also grown but have similar properties.
- Some data was not able to be secured

Group B

Name	Shrinkage % Tang	Unit	Durability Above ground	Class In ground	Hardness Seas Janka	Affect of Lyctus borer
Pine caribbean	5.0	0.34	4	4		NS
Celery top Pine	3.1	0.19	1		4.5	NS
Pine white Cypress	2.5	0.26	1	1	6.1	NS
Pine hoop	3.8	0.23	4	4	3.4	NS
Pine radiata	5.1	0.27	4	4	3.3	NS
Pine slash	4.2	0.30	4	4	3.4	NS
IMPORTED						
Balau	7.0	---	1	2	2.0	NS
Calantas	7.0	---	2	4	VS	S
Durian			4	4		S
Kapur	6.0	---	2	3	5.4	NS
Meranti Light red	4.4	---	4	4	2.4	S
Kwila/Merbau	2.5	---	2	3	8.8	S
Oregon	4.0	---	4	4	3.0	NS
Teak	4.0	---	1	2	---	S
Western red cedar	3.0	---	2	3	VS	NS

NOTES:

- Teak is classed in hardness as firm below moderately hard
- Unfortunately, not all the properties of some species were available.
- VS means very soft

Conclusion

As stated in the introduction the author's purpose in writing this book was to provide a handy reference in understandable language with as much reliable information as possible about timber and allied board products that could be covered in one book. By careful study and assimilation of the information provided in the *Essential Guide* the reader would be assisted in producing the desired outcome in any type of timber project whether it be big or small. However, there is no suggestion that the many projects that have already been carried out without the aid of this guide have not produced satisfactory results. The percentage of projects where serious problems occur is always small but, when they do happen, they can be costly and cause a lot of dissatisfaction. This is often due to a lack of understanding of all the properties and facets of the product. It was also hoped that the book could be used as an educational guide for beginners working with wood such as those in the Australian Men's Shed organization as well as a ready reference for those involved in carpentry and joinery courses.

The help that was received from so many people and organizations has been incredible and the author's thanks goes to all of them. In the Bibliography he has listed a number who have been particularly helpful especially those in the checking of the text. The author would welcome any suggestions on any amendments or extra sections that could be added if a revised addition was contemplated.

About the Author

Ed Scott spent the last 20 years of his working career before he retired in several management and technical positions in the plywood and timber industries. Some of these were as Queensland branch manager for Australia wide companies. Included in this was three years working in the Qld. Timber Research and Development Advisory Council [TRADAC]. This organisation assisted all who needed technical assistance and produced a wide range of technical bulletins covering correct procedures to be followed in different uses. Ed Scott has a degree in Science from the University of Qld. and completed the two-year Wood Technology course run by specialists from Qld. Forestry at the Brisbane Technical College.

Lightning Source UK Ltd.
Milton Keynes UK
UKHW031317260622
404944UK00003BA/65

9 781922 332875